BEASTS,
BANSHEES &
BOGEYMEN

For Brian Jacques
(1939-2011)

© Tom Slemen 2011
Published by The Bluecoat Press, Liverpool
Printed by Martins The Printers, Berwick
Cover illustration by Tom Slemen
Book design by March Graphic Design, Liverpool

ISBN 9781904438540

BEASTS, BANSHEES & BOGEYMEN

Tom Slemen

THE BLUECOAT PRESS

CONTENTS

BOGEYMEN

INTRODUCTION

This book, as the title plainly tells, is about beasts, banshees and bogeymen of Liverpool and Merseyside. What about the beasts of our title? Well, most of the mundane local history books do not contain any reference to the Werewolf of Speke Hall, nor do the tourist guide books mention the Beast of Bold Street, the Devil's Bridge, or the Black Elves of Bloody Acre. And no National Trust sightseeing handbook would advertise the Incubus of Edge Lane, the Hell Hound of Formby, or the Gargoyle of Crosby, but this book certainly will, and also explore possible explanations for the purported sightings and encounters.

As unbelievable as it may seem, within the staid and sober log reports of Merseyside Police, are to be found copious descriptions of some rather exotic and dangerous out-of-place animals and other beasts that are roaming our county. Police officers in recent years have been called out by the public in response to sightings and encounters with black panthers, lions, pumas and leopards. Here are just a few of these reports which came to light, thanks to the Freedom of Information Act: a puma being hunted by a police patrol after it was seen by scores of people roaming the thirteenth hole at Wirral Ladies Golf Club, Bidston Road – the big cat even left its paw prints on the green; a panther on the loose near Hooton Park Lane, seen by many people, including an expert on wild animals who was once employed by Chester Zoo; two golden lions seen cavorting around Southport's Mill Lane; an enormous black panther seen darting between the rocks on Egremont Promenade in Liscard; a puma that narrowly missed being knocked down by a lorry as it bolted across the M58; a leopard that was seen running up Bold Street at 6am chasing pigeons; and a six-foot-long panther that was seen slinking down the Loopline, a disused train-line linking Knowsley to Sefton.

There is a supernatural aspect to all of these big cat reports, in that none of them were captured, despite, in some cases, the police helicopter being deployed to track them down. Of course, Merseyside isn't at all unique, as regards to these big cat sightings. We only have to look at long-standing mysteries such as the Surrey Puma and the Beast of Bodmin, but the beasts of Merseyside are not all cats – some are much more outlandish than that.

The banshee is deemed a mere folklore character by most students of the paranormal, but I know better, as I have actually seen one with my own eyes and heard one as well. The name banshee is derived from the Gaelic words 'bean sidhe', meaning woman of the 'Shee' – or the faery folk.

Many years ago, in the 1980s, I went to post a letter one night, and took my dog Leo out with me, as he'd had virtually no exercise that day. As I passed an alleyway off Chatsworth Street, Edge Hill, I was startled to see a young woman crouched down on the pavement in the foetal position, with her knees drawn up to her face, which was bowed down and hidden by her long raven-black hair. Her clothes were all black, as well as her pointed shoes, and she was making a low mournful sound. My dog wasn't at all keen on the stranger, and his ears, which were usually upright and pointed, lay flat against his head, and the hair on his back reared up in a tuft. Leo was a muscular little dog, and he darted off, yanking me away from the crying woman.

I went to post the letter in the pillarbox, which was on the corner, just down the road, and when I returned a few minutes later, the woman had gone. I told my mother about the sobbing girl, and she glanced at the clock and said to me, 'So when you saw her, that would have been about 10.40pm?' I nodded. The next day, mother and I learned that a woman with an Irish surname had passed away at that very time – 10.40pm – and the crying lady in black had been sitting very close to the deceased woman's home. My mother told me I had seen a banshee, which was very rare, as they were heard more than they were seen.

On an earlier occasion, when I was about twelve, I was sleeping over at a schoolfriend's home in Myrtle Gardens, a tenement on the border of Edge Hill and Toxteth. I slept 'top-to-tail' in my friend's bed, but didn't get that much sleep during my stay because he was a fantastic storyteller who had a seemingly unending supply of strange tales, and even as he lay in bed, he insisted on narrating a series of gruesome yarns that prevented me from having a peaceful night's sleep.

At around 1.30am, he was in the middle of one of his stories when he was interrupted by a woman's terrifying screech. This woman was in the long dark passageway that ran under the my friend's flat, and her echoing howls and loud sobs shattered the quiet that had settled over the flats. We opened the bedroom window and looked out on to Melville Place. Curtains twitched in the houses opposite; other people had had their slumbers disturbed by the weird melancholic wailer. My friend's mother burst into the room in her nightdress and told us to get away from the window, and get back to bed immediately, which we did. She warned us not to look out of the window again, not saying why we shouldn't, but she certainly look terrified of something.

On the following day, we saw police cars parked down in Melville Place and an ambulance. We learned that an Irish prostitute had died at around one in the morning, choking on her own vomit after a drinking binge. Her flat was adjacent to the tenement passageway. Right away, people connected the wailing in the early hours with the death of the prostitute, and, to reinforce the connection, an elderly woman named Kate, one of the people in the houses opposite who had been peeping through the net curtains, had actually seen the woman in the passageway. 'She was a banshee, as true as God's in Heaven,' I recall her saying. 'She had long white hair, and was all in black. I couldn't see her face, because her head was bowed and her hair covered her features ... I slept with the light on after that.'

Then we come to the shady territory of the bogeyman, that eternal archetypal creature of the night who secretes himself at the back of wardrobes and under beds across the world. Know-it-all sociologists have long classified, stamped, and pigeon-holed the bogeyman as either a folklore figure, an imaginary 'friend', or a character invented by parents to keep their naughty children in check – but my years of research suggest otherwise. Some bogeymen (and bogeywomen) are all too real, and seem to have an independent existence – a life of their own – on the fringes of that vague territory we know as Reality.

There is a surprising concentration of bogeymen in Liverpool, and may I take the opportunity at this juncture to give warning to the more imaginative reader? Be careful when reading this book, because it may open up doors in your mind that took some effort to close when they were slammed in the face of things you encountered as a child. Those doors have been keeping the old bogeymen at bay for many years, and they may have given up on you by now, but you never can tell.

'The trouble with the world,' Bertrand Russell once quipped, 'is that the stupid are cocksure and the intelligent are full of doubt.' All of the experts nowadays are cocksure that there are no bogeymen, but true freethinkers on the subject allow a measure of doubt. 'Experts' were once certain that the Earth was at the centre of the universe, and that the sun and planets orbited our planet, until a freethinker called Copernicus discovered the truth. Similarly, experts such as Isaac Newton once stated that time was a mechanical, regular unalterable thing that ticked away monotonously everywhere in the universe at the same time, until Albert Einstein proved that time is elastic – it can be stretched and shrunk, and it flows at different rates in different parts of the cosmos. Before the invention of the microscope, who could have suspected that nightmarish-looking germs existed? The ghastly forms of the humble dust mite and other microscopic creatures were invisible to our eyes for millennia because they existed on a different plane of scale, so, for all we know, some terrifying creatures, long believed to be bogeymen, may one day be discovered to be living 'next door' to us in a neighbouring dimension. Perhaps, as you read these very words, beings separated from this reality by a wafer-thin partition of some higher dimension may be peering over your shoulder, perusing this sentence with a wry smile …

Tom Slemen, 2011

BEASTS

THE SPEKE HALL WEREWOLF

On Wednesday, 3 January 1855, Liverpool lay under a deep blanket of cast-iron-hard snow that had lain across Lancashire and the rest of the country since Christmas, and a thaw would be months away. On that bygone evening, John McFarlane, the land-steward to the Speke Hall estate, his beautiful daughter Ellen, and Thomas Edwards, an elderly friend of the McFarlanes, sat cosseted before a roaring log-fire in the parlour of Speke Hall. Christmas garlands still festooned the mantelpiece, and the keeper of Speke Hall was still recovering from the usual indulgences of Yuletide food and drink. Outside, a full moon hung over the tranquil lace-white landscape in which nothing moved.

Mr McFarlane was feeling a little charitable that night, and had invited his teenaged servants, William Parker and Mary Taylor, to the fireside, where they were treated to rum, whiskey, venison cutlets, mince pies and Eccles cakes, baked by Mrs Seddon, the hall's talented cook. At midnight, Constable Banks called at the grand Tudor house, and Ellen McFarlane and Mrs Seddon could both tell that he was not his usual jovial self. He looked troubled by something, and Ellen was the one who finally asked if he was alright. He nodded, held his outstretched hands to the rosy fire, and a tot of McFarlane's good whiskey soon loosened his tongue.

He thought he had seen something near Stockton Woods, a stone's throw from the hall, while on his beat earlier in the evening. At first he suspected it to be a poacher, but when he noticed the faint tracks in the snow, he realised they had been left by an animal with exceedingly elongated paws – about a foot in length in fact. The tracks ran into the woods, but Banks had felt too uneasy to follow and see where the trail led, and he also had a horrible feeling he was being watched by someone – or something.

On the way to Speke Hall, the well-liked local bobby had met an old farmer named Tindle, who was returning from the house of his cousin in Hale. On hearing Bank's description of the tracks, Tindle told him that he too had seen them many years ago – and the thing that had made them. The tracks had been made by a werewolf, according to the farmer. 'I thought it was all a load of rot but didn't like saying it,' Banks told his fireside friends, 'what, with him being old and that. A werewolf indeed! Have you ever heard anything so absurd?'

Mr McFarlane gravely admitted that he had indeed heard of the werewolf. Dark legends of such a supernatural creature roaming the manor of Speke had been circulating for generations, and the lycanthrope – as a werewolf was officially termed in the world of the occult, was believed to have actually been a local lecherous sixteenth century aristocrat – and the surname Lathom was always brought up whenever the strange stories were recounted. In all versions of the tales, the Lathom concerned had outraged the daughter of a Romany woman, who put a curse on him, which turned him into a beast when the moon was full. PC Banks feigned a chuckle, but his eyes were full of fear, and when he reluctantly departed at the witching hour of one o'clock, his eyes darted anxiously about, scanning the moonlit fields of snow.

Mr Edwards was more fortunate and decided to accept his friend's invitation to stay until morning, on account of the Arctic weather, not to mention the tales of a werewolf at large. He was being escorted to the guest bedroom by the servant boy William at 1.20am, when a blood-curdling howl rent the air throughout Speke manor. Ellen McFarlane flew to her bedroom window and there she saw what she believed to be a huge Irish wolfhound loping towards the snowman that had been built by the servants William and Mary earlier that day. But this was no dog, for it had no tail, and it reared up on two legs and savaged the snowman with its vicious jaws. Having scattered the hat, carrot-nose and coal eyes, the beast bolted towards the hall – before skidding to a halt and looking up directly at Ellen's window.

The girl froze for a moment, then dashed out of her room, bumping into her father John and Mr Edwards on the landing. She told them what she had seen, and her father ordered her to stay in her room. Mr McFarlane alerted his game-keeper Robert Smith, who quickly dressed and loaded his shotgun. Ellen hysterically begged her father not to confront the beast, which was obviously the werewolf he had spoken of earlier, but John McFarlane and the gamekeeper bravely ventured out into the silent silvered snowscape of Speke Hall's grounds – and at once were met by the grey abomination.

The creature looked like a wolf only it now stood tall on its two hind legs, like a human, towering to over six feet in height. It snapped and snarled at McFarlane, who stood there with his hand on his hip, confident that the beast would surely perish after a blast, at short range, from the gamekeeper's double-barrelled Cogswell & Harrison shotgun. But Gamekeeper Smith was trembling, for he sensed that the werewolf was a demonic manifestation that could not be despatched by the ordinary weapons of this world.

'Stay calm, Smith,' McFarlane whispered, 'and blast the blighter in the chest. Don't damage the head. We'll have this wretched thing stuffed and then see the faces on those know-alls in the Royal Society. We'll be rich, man.'

'Maybe we should go back inside, Mr McFarlane,' pleaded a perspiring, shaking Smith. 'Look at the eyes. They're devil eyes!'

The werewolf suddenly dropped down on to all fours and became as flat as a cat that's about to pounce. McFarlane gave the order to fire, but Smith was already turning away, ready to run back to the manor house. 'Fire, you coward!' McFarlane shrieked. As Smith ran, he slipped on the rock-hard snow. McFarlane didn't even see the werewolf pounce. Something thumped with enormous force against his back and sent him hurling face-down into the snow, badly winded. The man-beast then sprinted like the wind past the fallen gamekeeper and within a heartbeat was at the entrance to Speke Hall's kitchen. It turned the handle effortlessly and admitted itself into the Tudor mansion.

The servant boy, William Parker, froze when he saw the tall unearthly hair-covered figure with the head of a wolf and the eyes of a madman coming his way. The werewolf struck him with its huge clawed paw, knocking the lad sideways, unconscious. It tackled the stairs on all fours and began clawing at the bed-chamber door of Ellen McFarlane, who, faint with fear, hurriedly pushed a heavy cabinet against the door, then backed away. The heavy oaken door was almost being smashed off its hinges by the brute force being exerted upon it. Meanwhile, Mr McFarlane had picked himself up from the snow, and snatched the shotgun from the gamekeeper, who was stuttering out excuses for his cowardice. McFarlane then dashed into the house, just as the door to Ellen's bedroom finally yielded. Ellen collapsed on to the bed, and the werewolf leaned over her. It was stroking her long sandy hair when a sound like thunder shook the room, as two barrels were discharged by McFarlane into the brute's left shoulder-blade. The werewolf crumpled on to his intended victim, slobbering, groaning in agony.

The gamekeeper quickly appeared behind McFarlane and handed him two more cartridges. As the werewolf reared up and spun round to present its terrifying jaws, John McFarlane blasted it in the chest. The impact sent the lycanthrope crashing against the wardrobe with such force, its mirror shattered. Even then, the inhuman fiend still staggered to its feet, then dived through the window. It landed in the snow in a shower of blood and glass, and bounded off like a greyhound into the white moonlit wilderness of rural Speke.

Ellen took many months to recover from her ordeal, but instead of pushing the horrific incident to the back of her mind, she instead went to the library and read a great deal about werewolves. In fact, she became obsessed with them. Her father encouraged her to socialise, for she had become something of a recluse after the attack. And so Ellen reluctantly agreed to go to a dance in Halewood, and there became captivated by a lance corporal named Shaw, who lived locally. She fell madly in love with him, but soon noticed something odd about him – the third fingers on each of his hands were the same length as the second fingers – one of the marks of a werewolf. Shaw's eyebrows also met in the middle – another sure sign of a lycanthrope – and Ellen noticed how, whenever a full moon was due, Shaw would always go missing. In the end, Ellen voiced her suspicions to her lover, and Shaw reluctantly admitted to being a werewolf, and even showed Ellen the scars on his chest and left shoulder blade made by her father's shotgun the night he had entered her room. 'I had loved you before you even noticed me,' Shaw told Ellen, who instantly ceased to have anything to do with the lance-corporal.

Shaw, I have discovered, was the descendant of the illegitimate son of one Robert Lathom – the sixteenth century debauchee who was widely believed to be a werewolf. They say the seed of Lathom impregnated many a poor girl during his reign of terror, and today, his offspring could be anywhere, but hopefully the gene of the lycanthrope, if there is such a thing, has become diluted over the generations, but for all you know, you may be descended from werewolf stock yourself!

THE BEAST OF BOLD STREET

Bold Street in the witching hour can be as busy as noonday Piccadilly Circus, thanks to the twenty-four hour society we now find ourselves in. The nightlife of the popular thoroughfare is mostly concentrated around the clubs of Concert Square, but after the young nocturnal heathens have vacated the dens of dance and drink, an uneasy quietude often descends on the street, particularly on dark wintry mornings, and occasionally even during those bright vernal pre-dawn hours as well. It always begins with a calm before the storm – a soundless oasis surrounding the victim, and within this eerie hush, a long-forgotten menace from the past violently lunges into the present.

Again and again I have heard about a supernatural creature, a powerful brute of an animal that has chased and physically injured people with such force, they have been flung into the air and smashed against walls. I am still largely in the dark as to the nature of this brute, but I will venture to present a theory which may just throw some feeble light on what I will term the 'Beast of Bold Street'.

While most of the city slumbers, strange unfathomable things have been seen and heard on Bold Street; things that have turned burly eighteen-stone men into quivering wrecks. In a history-packed city such as ours, I have found that, under certain conditions, the past seems to reclaim that ephemeral quicksilver dimension-edge that we mortals, in our ignorance, like to term 'the present'.

Our first encounter with the Beast takes place in late October 1966. On a still autumnal morning at 4am, thirty-year-old newsagent Ron Castle left his flat on Chatham

Street (just off Myrtle Street), and headed for his shop on Bold Street. He was over an hour earlier than usual because he had woken with the niggling suspicion that he had not locked his shop up securely the night before. As he was passing the premises of a shop on Bold Street where Maggie May's Café is currently located, Ron suddenly felt as if he had walked into what he can only describe as a 'pocket of muteness'. He ceased to hear the taps of his own sole studs on the pavement, as if he were walking on a deep-pile carpet, which had muffled the sound. Then he heard something galloping behind him. The newsagent stopped in his tracks and turned round. He could plainly hear something snorting and grunting as it thundered in his direction at a terrific gallop, and although he could see nothing in the dark street, his instincts quickly told him to get out of the way of the unseen creature.

This was in an era when the ubiquitous steel roller shutter was rarely seen on any shop front, and in those innocent times, one could go window-shopping by moonlight, long after all the stores had closed. Ron jumped out of the way of the bestial demon by leaping into a shop doorway, and a split-second later, there was a massive gushing of displaced air as the beast beyond Ron's visual perception charged past. He stood, rooted in the doorway, unable to explain what was happening. He suspected the thing was some kind of ghost, but the ghost of what? For now, he could still hear the clattering of hooves on the pavement, and it sounded as if the thing was turning round, about to unleash another life-threatening attack. Ron Castle bolted from the doorway and sprinted across the road, towards Waring & Gillow's furniture store, in whose doorway he once more sought refuge.

At this point something very curious occurred. Ron

spotted the welcoming sight of a lone policeman on his beat, coming down Bold Street on the other side of the road. 'Oi! Hey there!' Ron shouted at the dark spot in the distance. A loud snorting sound echoed somewhere nearby, and Ron thought he saw the exhaled breath of the invisible animal near the kerb to his left. The thing was heard to bolt away and the sound of its hooves striking the ground indicated that it now had the police constable in its sights. The policeman halted, as if bracing himself for the onslaught, then suddenly ran off down Heathfield Street. Satisfied the apparitional animal was now fully distracted by its new target, Ron fled down Bold Street to his shop. Panting heavily, he fumbled with the keys, and kept looking to his left to check if the entity was returning. To his horror … it was!

It turned out that the door to Ron's shop had been left unlocked after all, as he had originally suspected, but Ron didn't know this, and so, when he turned the key, he actually locked the door. In blind panic he kept trying to turn the handle, and repeatedly pushed and pulled at it, and all the time he could hear the thundering hooves bearing down on him. At the last moment, Ron actually felt the vibrations of the bestial behemoth through the soles of his feet as the pavement shook, and in one swift unconscious movement he successfully turned the key in the lock, then twisted the handle. He almost fell into the dark interior, then slammed the door behind him and leaned against it.

Seconds later the door shook with a tremendous jolt as something hard struck it – as if the malevolent creature outside had horns. Then the sound of the hooves rumbled away up the street. The newsagent stood in the dark for a while, trying to make sense of what he had just experienced, but found himself at a loss. He lit a cigarette, inhaled deeply, and peeped out of the window, concerned for any other early risers who might be strolling down the street. He hoped to catch sight of that policeman who had also been chased by the creature, but he never did, nor did he ever again hear the pounding hooves of that weird monstrous beast after that day.

From that day onward, Ron always made doubly sure that he had locked up properly, and never again went to his shop until the sun was up.

~

A woman who worked in the gas showrooms on Bold Street told me how, one morning in the winter of 1979, she was walking to work around 8am, when suddenly, the traffic noise at the busy junction of Berry Street, Leece Street and Renshaw Street, suddenly faded away. At this time in the morning, there was a handful of people walking nearby at the top of Bold Street, yet the sounds of their footsteps also suddenly stopped. The woman then felt what she took to be some animal's head, from the sheer force of it, pushing against the base of her back. She turned, but saw nothing. Then the invisible animal rammed into the woman's bottom with equal ferocity, tossing her up into the air like a rag doll. She bolted across the road, looking back in shock to see nothing there. She accosted a passer-by near the Asha restaurant and told him what had just happened. The man gave a knowing nod and said, 'Must have been the ghost.'

'A ghost? What d'you mean?'

'A few people have seen it,' the man replied. 'Did you actually see it? What was it like?'

The woman shook her head as she rubbed her sore

back. 'No, I didn't see it, but it attacked me all the same. Smashed into me twice … thought I was going to die.'

'It's supposed to be like a bull,' said the man, with a self-conscious raising of the eyebrows. Then, without elaborating further, he walked off, presumably on his way to work, leaving the bewildered woman nursing her buises and trying to make sense of the whole bizarre experience.

~

In 2003, nineteen-year-old Sheena had a row with Ian, her boyfriend of just three days, and stormed out of a club on Wood Street. The time was nearly 2am, and after Sheena had failed to hail a taxi on Ranelagh Street, she suddenly decided to go back in search of Ian to see if they could patch things up. After all, the argument had been over nothing and she really fancied him. She hoped to find him still at the club, but having described him to the bouncers, they said he had already left some time ago. For some reason, Sheena thought the doormen were lying, and she went on a fruitless search for Ian. She tried to call him but he'd switched his mobile off. Sheena wandered aimlessly around town, bumping into various friends from college, and one of them, a girl named Kelly, persuaded her to go to a party at a flat on Seel Street.

By around 4.15am, Sheena was in tears. She wanted to be with Ian, and against Kelly's wishes, she left the Seel Street flat in a drunken state and went looking for him. She thought she had spotted him at the bottom of Bold Street, and shouted after him, but when the young man turned around, Sheena immediately realised she was mistaken. The lad came over and started chatting to her and soon asked her to come back to his place. 'No, my boyfriend's waiting up here for me,' Sheena said, pointing up Bold Street.

'No he isn't,' said the pushy youth, and he grabbed Sheena's wrist, but she slapped him across the face and got her mobile out, threatening to call the police if he didn't leave her alone. The lad swore at her and ran off.

Sheena staggered up Bold Street and stopped at the corner of Slater Street and looked at the sad clear glowing screen of her phone. There was Ian's name, and she pressed the call button, but the voice of the automated operator told her that the person she was trying to call had their phone switched off. And then, despite not having experienced the 'quiet zone' reported by so many other people, Sheena saw what was unmistakably the enigmatic Beast – and it sobered her up in one heart-stopping moment.

Planted there in the shadows of that short passage named Newington, was a gigantic muscular bull, just a few yards to the left of the Old Rope Walk public house. Sheena is five foot six, and was wearing four-inch-platforms, and yet she still felt dwarfed by the out-of-place animal. She tried to pretend she hadn't noticed it, and quickly hurried up Bold Street, whispering a garbled prayer to herself. She looked back – the colossal Taurean creature had suddenly broken into a trot, and so Sheena quickly tried to hide behind a parked van. She was about to phone the police when she heard a familiar voice that lifted her spirits and momentarily made her forget about the massive bull.

'Shee!' Ian shouted, coming down Bold Street from the direction of Berry Street. 'What're you doing down there?'

'Oh, Ian, I've been looking everywhere for you,' she cried. 'Get down here! Out of the way of the bull.'

He thought she was going to deliver the punchline to

some joke, but Sheena clutched the front of his shirt and dragged him down beside her.

'Keep down, or it'll see us,' she hissed, cowering halfway under the van's bumper.

'Have you been taking anything?' asked Ian, puzzled, gazing into Sheena's tearful eyes.

'It's down there!' she cried, urgently nodding towards Newington, 'and no, I haven't been taking anything. What d'you take me for?'

More to show her that there was nothing to be afraid of than anything else, Ian walked off down the street but pulled up short on the corner of Newington. 'Oh my God! There it is! It's dancing!'

'What?' Sheena asked, peeping round the side of the van. 'Is it still there? Come back, Ian, or it'll get you.'

Ian ran back to her and kissed her, and then laughed, 'I'm only kidding, Shee, there's no bull there, you soft thing.'

It took a long time before Sheena would accept that the fearsome-looking animal had actually gone. It had apparently vanished into thin air. She was very badly shaken by the whole affair and even today, she won't venture near Bold Street after dark.

Sheena's case is unusual, in that she actually saw the animal, whereas most of the other witnesses I have talked to only heard the sound of the beast, or felt it push against them. There are a couple of exceptions though; a security guard who looks after premises in the Bold Street area said he saw a large dark brownish shape moving along Slater Street from the direction of Bold Street one morning at around 4.30am. Another guard working for a separate security firm vindicated this sighting independently, and also reported seeing an amorphous reddish-brown shape moving along Bold Street on the following night with his own eyes and also caught it on a CCTV camera.

Bold Street has had an unusually high incidence of timeslips, and anyone who reads my books and columns will be aware of this. There are many theories as to why these timewarps are so prevalent on the street, including one which hypothesises that the high-tension electrified railway line running parallel to Bold Street may produce a disturbance in time akin to the relativistic effects which high-energy velocities have on the fabric of space-time in the form of time-dilation. Some even believe that the sandstone of the Lyceum building, at the bottom of Bold Street – the epicentre of the timeslips – may be vibrating like a giant quartz crystal, because of the electromagnetic fields of nearby Central Station.

If the 'Beast of Bold Street' is in fact a time-slipped bull from the days of rural Liverpool, or even a prehistoric bovine creature, then it would explain why it appears and seemingly disappears into thin air, as well as its longevity. Researching this case, I chanced to come across the following article, which appeared in the *Liverpool Mercury* newspaper, dated 15 December 1820:

A FATAL ACCIDENT

On Saturday last, about noon, a bullock, just landed from a vessel, escaped from the King's Dock, and, for upwards of two hours, ran furiously through a considerable part of the town before it could be secured. It is our painful duty to record several accidents, in consequence of a more serious nature than the dispersion and confusion of the people, who, it being market day, crowded several streets through which the enraged animal

27

took its way. After causing considerable alarm, it ran at a woman in Colquitt Street, who escaped its fury by throwing her basket at its head, to which its rage was immediately diverted. In Bold Street, it rushed at the female servant of a lady residing there, whom it tossed and gored in so dreadful a manner, that she expired while being carried to the Infirmary. It attacked a man in the same street, and tore open his cheek; the sufferer narrowly escaped by taking refuge in a doorway in Church Street. In Church Street it threw down two ladies, one of whom, falling under a cart that was passing, was severely bruised. In Tarleton Street, it sprang from the middle of the pavement to the parapet, and overturned a lady and a man, dispersing and terrifying others.

The bull, destined for the slaughter house, was eventually captured and killed. In my long experience of delving into all things paranormal, I have often encountered the ghosts of animals, and anyone who says that cats and dogs, even budgerigars, don't have souls, doesn't know what he or she is talking about. All living things have a soul, but if we accept this it opens up all sorts of uncomfortable ethical problems concerning our sources of food and so on.

The bull has featured as a subject for artists and mystics for thousands of years. The aurochs bull is depicted in the famous 17,000-year-old cave paintings at Lascaux in France, and as far back as 2150 BC the mystical Bull is featured in one of the human race's earliest works of literature: the Sumerian Epic of *Gilgamesh*, where we read of the venerated Bull of the Heavens. Of course, the bull is also one of the ancient mysterious signs of the Zodiac – Taurus.

Is the spirit of a slaughtered bull haunting Bold

Street, or is a bull from the days when the city centre was a rustic patchwork of fields trapped in some space-time limbo that is connected to the many paranormal timeslip anomalies that exist around Bold Street?

SABBAXA

The following is a true story, related to me many years ago, and it took place in the 1990s.

About twice a month, but always on a busy Saturday, fifty-four-year-old Louise would stroll into Liverpool's most well-known store and select a fairly expensive dress or a pair of shoes, and expertly remove the price labels on the chosen items. She would then approach the counter of the most naive-looking shop assistant she could find and say something along the rehearsed lines of, 'This isn't suitable for the person I bought it for. I'd like a refund please.'

The assistant would often ask for a receipt, and Louise would reply, 'I can't find it, but as you can see, I obviously purchased this item here.'

And the assistant would always nod and say words to the effect of: 'Yes, of course, that's our brand,' or the difficult ones would say, 'I'm sorry but we can't offer a refund, just an exchange,' so Louise would either storm out with the free expensive dress or shoes, or she would choose another, similar item. And that was just one scam, in one store. There were other, daily deceptions in other stores, and some of Louise's tricks amounted to the legerdemain of the Magic Circle calibre. Furthermore, Louise's nineteen-year-old son, Paul, was an able pickpocket, and one spring morning, he mingled with the shoppers in WH Smith who were huddled in rows in front of the store's extensive magazine section, and Paul's grandfather, George, provided the usual distraction to the victims. On this occasion George took down a 'top shelf' magazine and opened it at the centre pages, ogling the nude centre-spread at arms length in the way long-sighted people do. 'God, look at that!' he quipped. 'She can't be real – look at the size of them!'

A well-to-do woman glared at the apparently lecherous old man and ushered her young nephew away from the shockingly graphic magazine picture. Paul had already been down her pockets, only to find her purse wasn't there. It had probably been in the woman's handbag, and so he moved on to the other magazine browsers as his grandfather threw the magazine back up on to the top shelf with the exclamation 'Filth!'

Then the old man stumbled a few times and pretended he was drunk, and eventually when he left WH Smith, he rendezvoused with his grandson at Quiggins, that much-missed back-street emporium on School Lane. On this Saturday, George and Paul met up with Louise, who had decided to actually legally buy something from Quiggins, instead of using her crooked sophistry and underhand tricks to dupe the retailers out of their wares – but old habits die hard, and grandfather, daughter and grandson weren't in Quiggins long when Louise saw something she just had to have. A tall Gothic-looking gentleman with a greying van dyke beard, a dark ruby-coloured polo-neck sweater, over which he wore a well-cut black knee-length jacket, was lighting up his purple-papered cheroot (when it was legal to do so before the smoking ban), and Louise immediately fell in love with his silver lighter, because it featured an embossed devil upon it.

Louise wasn't into Satanism, but she loved unusual lighters, and this one was just begging to be stolen. The Goth who owned the silver lighter was a Welshman who was not exactly old but was definitely past his prime, and his name was Aneurin Sly, said by some to be a very eccentric but learned man. On this April day he was asking a young vermilion-haired lady running a second-hand shop if she still had the statue of Baphomet he had seen days before. She hadn't, she was sorry to say, as someone had purchased it, and she couldn't get hold of another one. Louise pulled Paul and her father aside and told them quickly, in hushed tones, what she wanted, and in no time, Grandfather George had sprung into action. He approached Sly, seized his sleeve and said, 'Correct me if I'm wrong, but is that a Tonypandy accent?'

'No,' Sly replied, a little startled, 'I'm from Milford Haven.'

George gave a loud false laugh and said, 'Oh, I'm sorry.' Then he pitched another distraction as Paul lifted the lighter from the Welshman's coat pocket. 'That statue you were looking for – I think I saw one like it.'

'Oh really? Where was that?' Aneurin Sly asked, but his eyes darted sideways to Louise, who was watching her son pocket the purloined lighter she coveted so much.

George let go of Sly's sleeve and scratched the top of his trilby as he pretended to rack his brains. 'It was in a place in Chester; what's the name of that shop now?' He turned to Louise and asked her, 'Can you remember it? That antiques shop?'

'Sorry I can't,' was Louise's barely audible reply, and she turned and walked out of the unit and headed for the stairs with Paul.

'Memory loss is a terrible thing isn't it?' George said,

trying to look vacant, 'but that shop was definitely in Eastgate Street … I think.'

'No problem,' said Sly, and he inhaled the cheroot, and then nodded, saying, 'thanks anyway.'

George met his daughter and grandson outside on School Lane. The unholy trinity went to a café in the Bluecoat Chambers, and there Louise examined the lighter. 'Sterling silver,' she said, flicking open its top. She thumbed the wheel and a steady blue flame appeared from which she lit her Players cigarette. She then began to scrutinise the embossed cross-legged devil with her grey-blue eyes. He looked fearsome with his bull horns, pointed ears, and mouth full of triangular teeth. The eyes seemed to have an evil penetrating quality about them.

'Let's have a look, Mum,' Paul said, reaching over the table, with an intact digestive in the other hand.

'Look with your eyes, not your hands,' his mother told him, holding the lighter towards him but just out of his reach.

'He looks really weird to me,' Paul decided. 'Why did you want him anyway?'

'Oh, you know me,' Louise replied, with a faint smile, 'I'm a magpie. How much did you get?'

'Just under a ton, about ninety-five quid,' Paul estimated, but then he decided to check the exact amount he'd pick-pocketed and took the crumpled notes out of his pocket and counted them with a quick shuffle under the table. 'Yeah, ninety-five,' he confirmed.

'Marks and Sparks next, or Littlewoods?' Grandfather wondered out loud.

That night, just after twelve, Louise switched off the television set in her West Derby home and went to bed. Paul was staying over at his friend's house on Aldwark

Road, Dovecot, and her father George was still out drinking at a lock-in at the local pub. Louise had been divorced for two years, and at this time in her life she was not seeing or seeking anyone. She felt she'd had enough of men for the foreseeable future, especially after living with a self-righteous man like Tony for the last eighteen years. He had constantly criticised her lifestyle, and had wanted her to apply her brains to a nine-till-five job.

Louise was soon fast asleep in bed, but at around a quarter-past one that morning, she heard a heavy thump which startled her from her dreamless sleep, and when she opened her eyes, the bed was vibrating from a powerful low-pitched sound that seemed to be shaking the house to its foundations. She sat up, thinking an earthquake had struck West Derby. Bottles of perfume, jars of beauty cream and various ornaments rattled along the dresser and crashed to the floor. The ceiling lamp swung wildly from side to side, and then all of a sudden, the seven-foot-tall mahogany wardrobe toppled over and crashed on to the bed, narrowly missing a screaming Louise. An expensive antique rosewood chest of drawers, purchased with her ill-gotten gains, then launched itself across the room and smashed into the bedside cabinet, throwing the lamp and its shade on to the floor. Then something which would give Louise nightmares for the next three years occurred.

The bedroom door crashed inwards into the poorly-lit room, and a bulging figure squeezed through the splintered doorframe. By the feeble light of a mercury-vapour street-lamp shining into the room, Louise could make out that he looked just like the devil on her lighter; so tall, well over seven feet in height, that its horns scraped against the ceiling, and its eyes burned as two

33

crimson points of light. The monstrosity's heavy hooves pounded down on the floor, the ensuing vibrations travelling up through Louise's bare feet. The beast's powerful hands picked up the heavy king-sized bed and flipped it over in an effort to get at Louise, who slipped out of his grasp and bolted through the vacant doorway. She ran downstairs, opened the door, and ran blindly down the short garden path where she bumped into her father George (who was returning from the lock-in), knocking him into a bush.

Louise was so consumed with terror, she left her father there, prostrate, and ran off blindly down the street. She stopped at one point and looked up to her bedroom window, from where she could hear the sounds of the horned entity tearing her room apart. Neighbours came out to see what was happening, and when Louise gave an incoherent account of the thing trashing her bedroom, a well-meaning neighbour called the police, who promptly arrived in force in three squad cars. By then, Louise had mustered up enough courage to go and pick up her father, who was quite drunk and still stunned and bloodied from the fall into the bushes.

The police found no one in the house to account for the heavy damage to Louise's furniture, but they could not fail to detect the putrid sulphuric odour that had pervaded the bedroom. Then a detective noticed a number of discarded wallets and credit cards in one of the dresser drawers, a discovery that was to be the undoing of the felonious family. Before they were taken away and charged, Louise made a point of searching for the silver lighter with the strange demonic idol, but it was nowhere to be found.

After Louise and Paul and grandfather had served

their prison sentences, they happened to bump into Aneurin Sly one afternoon at a café in Southport, and he sneered at the trio, then produced the silver lighter from his pocket and proceeded to light his cheroot. Not a word was spoken.

Alas, the players of this strange episode have, rather strangely, all passed away from this arena of bustling life, but shortly before his death, Aneurin Sly showed the intriguing silver lighter to a friend, who photographed it for me. The demon embossed upon its case is Sabbaxa, allegedly one of the most powerful of the ancient demons. Sly bragged that Sabbaxa was easy to evoke simply by reciting three lines of spoken magic, and that he was a very loyal and affectionate entity. My friend asked the Welshman if he had sent Sabbaxa to retrieve the lighter that bore his image, and Sly said: 'No, I could only conjure him up by holding the lighter, but somehow, because he missed me so much, he manifested himself and then brought the lighter back to me.'

The present whereabouts of that silver lighter are unknown.

THE TARBOCK APE

A species of hominid, unknown to science, at large in the Cronton and Widnes area may sound like something from a Monty Python sketch, but over the years I have received so many consistent reports of this creature, which is, by all accounts, very similar to the descriptions of the giant ape-like Sasquatch – the American Bigfoot. The great anatomist Sir Arthur Keith once quipped that the only class of beings that are constantly reported, but never brought to the dissecting table must belong to the world of spirits, but contrary to the general view, our planet has not been fully explored, and there are still nineteen million square miles of the earth's surface that have not been investigated, so there is no sound zoological reason why an unknown beast should not be found, in say, the equatorial rain-forests of central Africa, or the frozen forests of Siberia. Satellite cameras routinely scan the earth each day, but even they have their limitations, and cannot penetrate deep enough into jungles, or beneath the seas. They certainly cannot see under the surface of the earth, where unknown subterranean creatures may have their lairs.

The famous naturalist, Baron Georges Cuvier, confidently stated in 1812, that, 'There is little hope of discovering a new species of large quadruped.' Just four years after Cuvier's remark, Governor Farquar, of the Asiatic Society, discovered the Tapir, a herbivore, previously unknown to science, living in the forests of Malaysia. Other animals have been discovered since Baron Cuvier's premature assertion, including the giant panda, the Manchurian Kodiak bear, the Komodo Dragon and so on. Admittedly these exotic animals were found in poorly-explored areas of the world's wilderness – not in the green expanses of suburban Widnes, and yet this is the area where a strange giant man-beast has been seen repeatedly over the years. Let us examine these sightings in chronological order.

One fine summer's afternoon in July 1961, David Halcraft, a twenty-four-year-old student from Liverpool University, set off cycling with his girlfriend Sandra Fraser from Childwall, where David's mother lived. The couple cycled eastwards along Netherley Road, then turned northwards up a rather secluded road named Cross Hillocks Lane, on the peripheries of Prescot and Widnes. The lane was bordered on each side by a hedge, and through several breaks in this hedge, David and Sandra could see the shimmering green and brown patchwork quilt of farmland. The only sound in this calm rural setting was the whirring from the gears of the two bicycles, and the odd drone of a passing bee. But halfway down the secluded lane, Sandra suddenly heard a faint padding sound coming up behind her, and she turned to see what it was.

A giant male human figure, about seven feet in height, and covered from head to ankles in dark brown fur, was running down the lane towards the cyclists. Hearing Sandra's screams, David looked round, and he too saw the hairy Goliath, who was bounding towards them with an evil-looking smile on his gorilla-like face. Sandra's legs felt weak with shock, but David urged her to pedal as fast as she could to outdistance the terrifying wild-man. Somehow, she managed to increase her speed, but the man-beast seemed to be steadily upon them, and the padding of his huge feet was getting louder. Sandra began to cry when the gargantuan figure came within twenty feet of her bike. She could hear the monster grunting and panting, but was too scared to look back in case she lost speed. This went on for almost half a mile until the lane branched off into Stockswell Road. At the bridge that crossed Dog Clog Brook, David looked back and saw that the furry giant figure had gone to ground somewhere.

Sandra became so distressed she suffered an asthma attack, and for some time after the incident, she suffered nightmares about being chased by the mysterious beastly pursuer, and never again ventured anywhere near Netherley Road or Cross Hillocks Lane. When David told his mother about the incident, she deepened the mystery by revealing that her late grandfather had told her about a hairy wild-man who had once chased him and two friends when they were children playing in fields near Tarbock Hall, around the turn of the twentieth century. David researched the history of Tarbock, but could find no account of the fearsome-looking 'ape' being seen in the area.

Then, one blustery March evening in 1970, Jim Rylands and Peter Sheraton, two nineteen-year-olds from Court Hey, went out for a spin in a dilapidated Vauxhall Victor, Jim having just passed his driving test. Jim set out with no particular destination in mind, but by 9.30pm had decided, on his friend Peter's suggestion, to go looking for some female company in a pub in Cronton. 'Birds love cars,' Jim reminded his friend with a proud smile.

'Yeah, cars, not old bangers,' laughed Peter.

'Oh shurrup. Where's your motor then? You can't even drive.'

The lads carried on in this vein until Jim said, 'What's the name of this pub anyway? Bet you've never even been.'

Peter couldn't recall the name of the pub he had in mind, but assured Jim the girls he'd seen in that 'country boozer' were absolutely beautiful. Jim had no clear idea where Cronton was, so did his best to follow the road-signs, and by 10pm, he and Peter rejoiced when they discovered they had reached Cronton Road. Unfortunately, at this point, the Vauxhall Victor's worn-out engine started to make strange noises, and the car stuttered to a gradual halt. Jim took a look under the bonnet, even though he hadn't a clue what he was looking for. The engine seemed very hot and he inspected the fan belt, 'Get out me way, Pete. You're blocking out the light from that lamp-post.'

'Sorry, mate. I was only trying to help.'

Just then a car came past, and slowed till it pulled up behind their car. An elderly man in a tweed jacket and flat cap got out and asked the teenagers if he could be of any help.

'Oh, yes please,' said Jim, 'it was making a funny noise and the engine's boiling hot.'

The old man made a cursory examination of the engine, then quickly deduced the problem. In a stern low voice he said, 'The tappets are knackered, lad, and you've also got a leaking water hose. I can do nowt about the tappets, but I might be able to fix the hose ... hang on.'

'Thanks, mate,' said Peter, and he and Jim watched the kind old motorist return to his car, and fetch a small tool kit from the boot. He fitted a worm-drive clip to replace the old rusty clip, and then patched up a few cracks in the hose with adhesive tape. When he had finished, the silvery-haired Samaritan said, 'That's the hose fixed, now you should be able to get home, but those tappets are in a terrible state. If you lose power, just pull over and let the engine cool for a bit, then start it again.'

The lads thanked the old man and reluctantly decided to abandon their plans for meeting the belles of Cronton, and headed home. Peter said he knew a short-cut, and advised Jim to drive down the almost pitch-black Alder Lane. As the car neared the junction of Dog Clog Bridge, the engine steadily lost power, just as the old man had predicted. The Vauxhall Victor cruised to a gentle halt. Jim put the handbrake on and sat there, sighing with frustration. A full moon suddenly emerged from the clouds and cast its silvery-blue light on the lonely lane and surrounding fields.

Peter saw it first. 'Who's that?' he asked, pointing to

a silhouette about two-hundred yards down the lane. A gargantuan man was walking towards them with a very peculiar lolloping gait. A sudden gust of wind which briefly howled around the car only served to heighten the spooky atmosphere.

'God! The size of him!' gasped Jim, as the moon slid behind a cloud, cutting off virtually all the reassuring light from the surrounding area. Jim flicked on the headlamps, which lit up the lane as far as Dog Clog Bridge. The giant had gone. A few minutes passed and Jim started the engine again. The power had returned, if only for a while, and he drove off, over the bridge that spanned the little brook, and on to Cross Hillocks Lane, where, once again, the troublesome tappets caused the engine's power to slowly ebb away. The moon came out again. Jim banged the steering wheel and swore; he'd be having words with the man who had sold him the car first thing in the morning.

'How much did you say it cost you?' Peter asked.

'Fifteen quid,' Jim replied, 'but that's not the point, it's a total lump of scrap.'

Something caught his eye in the rear-view mirror – that giant shadowy figure again. It was plodding down the moonlit lane, and already, from a distance of about a hundred yards, Jim could see there was something not quite right about this stranger in the night. He seemed to be covered in hair all over his body, except for his odd-looking face and his bare feet below the ankles. Jim swore and drew his friend's attention to the alarming figure approaching from behind.

'Quick! Start the car! Let's get out of here NOW!' Peter screamed, the tension unbearable as Jim desperately tried to start the car. The Vauxhall Victor was having none of it. Jim pressed his foot down on the accelerator – nothing. Peter threw open the passenger door, jumped out the car, and ran off down the lane like a frightened hare into the gloom, just as the moon again disappeared behind a cloud. In the meantime, the simian-like figure drew nearer, and when it was about twenty feet away, Jim tried the engine again, and this time the car, which had been left in first gear, lurched forward. He drove off down the lane with the passenger door still wide open. He overtook Jim, then tried to reverse so he could get back in the car, but as he accelerated backwards, his inexperience quickly showed, and he lost control of the car, which curved in its trajectory, and the open passenger door hit the small stump of a tree that had been recently cut down. The stump wrenched the door clean off. Somehow, Peter managed to jump into the car, which careered off down the lane, with him clinging to his seat, unable even to fasten his safety-belt to stop him falling out of the speeding car. Jim checked his rear-view mirror. The silhouetted figure picked up the wrenched-off car door and slammed it into a ditch, then waved its long arms in the air.

The car eventually reached Childwall after many more power-loss episodes, and refused to start again, so they abandoned it, and when they went to look for it in the morning, it had gone. 'Good riddance! What a load of junk!'

'What d'you expect for fifteen quid, a Merc?'

The two lads burst out laughing.

'What a night! Joking apart, what the hell was that thing? I've never seen anything like it.'

'No idea, but I'm in no hurry to go back and find out.'

Jim later acquired a more reliable set of wheels in the

form of a mini, but he never ventured anywhere near that remote lane where he had encountered the strange giant hairy man.

In the severe winter of 1981, several people in the areas of Tarbock and Prescot found a trail of footprints leading across snow-covered fields adjacent to Cross Hillock Lane, apparently made by enormous human feet, which must have belonged to a giant. Student hoaxers were suspected, but no one ever claimed responsibility.

Then, one night, in June 1985, a motorist travelling along Cronton Road, heading towards Liverpool, almost collided with a huge man covered with reddish-brown hair near the junction of Fox's Bank Lane. The giant figure 'with a pointed head and a huge jawbone' bolted across the road from the direction of the Brick Wall public house, and was seen by several other people that night peeping over a hedge. On that occasion, hoaxers were again blamed, but in the 1990s, sightings of the enigmatic humanoid creature continued.

At 9.30pm one pleasant evening in August 1992, two eighteen-year-old sisters painting watercolour landscapes, encountered a fur-clad figure in Water Lane, a mere stone's throw from Dog Clog bridge, where most of the sightings have taken place. The petrified pair ran all the way home to Cronton to tell their parents, but despite a search, the creature was never found.

Around this time there was another report of a thirteen-year-old boy who saw the creature near Alder Lane, and far from being scared of it, he claimed he had offered it his Mars Bar, and the creature had stooped down and snatched it from him before running off!

There is obviously a paranormal element to these sightings. He seems real enough to leave footprints in the snow (and on one occasion, alleged faeces containing the remains of berries), and yet, when an immediate search is made to find this 'Missing Link', he seems to vanish into thin air, just like his American cousin Bigfoot, and Tibetan relative, the Yeti, and therein lies the dual mystery of the 'Cronton Ape'. Is this creature a Neanderthal or a Cro-Magnon man from the misty forests of ancient Lancashire? If so, how did he fall out of the tree of human evolution into our epoch? Is a localised timeslip to blame, or is there a deep, mystical nature-rooted aspect to this mystery? Is the Tarbock Ape as real as the legendary Green Man nature spirit, or the Mowing Devil of old England who was recorded in the seventeenth century creating what we now call corn circles? The countryside still harbours her green mysteries, and long may they endure.

THE DOG MAN

Across Liverpool, in the late 1970s and early 1980s, there was a rather strange and alarming character at large, rumoured to be some kind of man-animal hybrid. The children of the northern purlieus of Liverpool had a nickname for him, Boris, for reasons best known to themselves, and the juvenile gangs of south Liverpool chose to call the same grotesquely weird vagrant, the Dog Man, for two reasons. Firstly, he was a man who seemed to be half, or part, animal, with a tail and nose like those found on a canine, and secondly, he roamed the industrial wastelands left in the wake of the slum-clearance bulldozers with a loyal pack of attendant mongrel dogs.

The Dog Man always wore a beret to cover a small pair of horns that jutted from his high forehead and a livid, unhealed, crudely stitched-up wound that ran from his bushy grey joined-up eyebrows to the back of his head. Children, as well as adults had seen the horns and the ghastly stitched head wound.

Horns that grow from human heads are more common than you may think, and we need only leaf through the local history books to learn of the strange condition of Mary Davies, the so-called 'Horned Woman of Saughall', who was born in Shotwick in 1600. Mary was a beautiful young girl when she married a Saughall man named Henry, and all went well with the marriage until, at the age of twenty-eight, she noticed that two lumps had appeared on her scalp, positioned symetrically at either side of her head. Medical advice was sought, but the local physician admitted bafflement and speculated that the lumps had perhaps been caused by Mary wearing hats that were a size too small. Mary was not convinced, as her hats fitted perfectly well.

In 1641, Mary's husband passed away, which meant she no longer had his sixteen pounds a year wage to rely on, so to support herself she decided to become a midwife. By now, the lumps on her head were becoming far more pronounced and pointed, projecting out one-and-a-half inches from behind her ears. By the time Mary was in her fifties, these horns had not only grown astonishingly long, but had also curved round in a way that made them resemble the horns of a ram.

Five more years passed and the horns loosened and dropped off, but not long after Mary had rejoiced at their loss, she discovered, to her great chagrin, that a new set had started growing in their place. The pair of horns that Mary had shed were obtained by a local nobleman, who presented them as a gift to King Louis XIV of France, who was fascinated by the ivory-like appendages. The authenticity of the Horned Woman of Saughall is further evinced by her portrait, executed when Mary was sixty-eight, which was displayed for many years in the Ashmolean Museum in Oxford.

But what was the nature of these horns? The

superstitious believed such protrusions indicated a demonic connection with the Devil, although everyone acquainted with Mary Davies knew her to be a kind and gentle soul. The physicians were at a loss to explain them, and while some believed the horns to be hardened skin, formed from the fibrous protein keratin, from which our nails are made, other men of medicine believed them to be made of an unknown material akin to ivory. Not a trace of Mary's horns exists today, so their mysterious nature and true composition remains unknown.

The horns that were said to protrude from the forehead of the Dog Man may have been similar to those of Mary Davies, but his nose was equally strange, because the tip of it was dark, leathery and wet, resembling that of a canine. The Dog Man was also reported to have a tail, but this might have simply been a mere urban legend (although many people I interviewed swore the tail was real), or he may have simply worn a belt of rope with a long dangling end that was perceived as a tail in the dark.

Of course, as with the horns, there are medical conditions in which otherwise healthy humans can develop a rudimentary tail or even be born with one that is an extension of the coccyx. The tail of the Dog Man was consistently described by many as being about two feet in length, and covered in sandy-brown and grey fur.

One of the earliest reports of the Dog Man dates back to sometime in 1974, on the Falkner housing estate which once existed off Myrtle Street, close to the Myrtle Gardens tenements. A strange-looking tramp with a motley pack of about a dozen or more dogs, walked into Garrets Butchers, a shop that was actually built into the Myrtle Gardens complex, and without saying a word, using only gestures and grunts, the old butcher understood that he was asking for any spare bones. Mr Garret gave the tramp a large bag of pork shoulder blades, ribs, various other bones, and sometimes the crackling too; the remnants and leftovers from the previous week. Satisfied, the tramp then walked across Myrtle Street, holding up the traffic as the hounds of his convoy trotted after him, sniffing the meaty aroma trailing through the air.

The Dog Man entered the Falkner housing estate, and immediately two youths began to make fun of his appearance, One snatched the beret from his head, revealing the gaping scar of clotted blood and ugly thick stitches, and of course the horns. Quick to retaliate, the tramp set the dogs on the mischief-making duo, and one of them received so many bites he had to be hospitalised. The Dog Man retrieved his beret and crossed the estate, passing by a public house called the Red Duster, and here, a tall Caribbean cousin of the youth who had been savaged by the dogs made the mistake of obstructing the king of the hounds, and the Dog Man seized the man's arm and sank his sharp ghastly-looking teeth into his forearm, drawing a fair quantity of blood. With Herculean strength, the tramp then threw the screaming man against the door of the pub, badly winding him.

The dogs immediately set upon the doubled-up gasping vigilante, and he too sustained as many bites as his young cousin, and was subsequently taken to Sefton General Hospital. By the time the police arrived, the Dog Man had allegedly gone to ground in the caves of Sefton Park. Being but a young child at the time, and living off Myrtle Street, I personally remember the various accounts of the incident. It was the talk of the neighbourhood for a while.

Sifting through the many letters and emails I have received about the leader of the dog-pack over the years, we next come to a violent encounter with the horned and tailed vagrant up on Love Lane, amidst the empty warehouses of Vauxhall, in that well-remembered infernal summer of '76 and the drought that resulted.

On a stretch of industrial wasteland covered with half-burnt palliasses, torn black rubbish bags, rusted bedsteads, the odd burnt-out car and other eyesores, the Dog Man sat, gnawing on a bare bone from a leg of lamb on a ragged plot of wild long grass faded to baby-blue by the harsh ultraviolet rays of that cruel sun. The children shouted names at the Dog Man, but this time he did not react, because he was too engrossed in extracting the marrow from the juicy bones and swiping away bluebottles. The group of children couldn't believe their eyes, and roared with laughter, because the vagrant had stripped down to a pair of shorts, and the only bare skin to be seen upon his person was on his face, hands and feet. The rest of the Dog Man's body was covered in a coat of mottled grey and light-brown hair like a hyena's, but as thick as any to be found on a border collie.

Sitting in an almost protective circle around the derelict, was his faithful pack of mongrels, tongues lolling, stretched out and listless in the unbearable heat. On this occasion, a gang of skinheads are said to have set upon the freakish-looking drifter with chains and knuckledusters. One of the stray dogs died in the attack, and although the Dog Man sustained what seems to have been a serious head injury, he fractured three ribs of one his attackers and bit part of another's finger clean off. One of the dogs was booted into the Leeds and Liverpool Canal but was rescued by two animal-lovers who saw the animal thrashing about as it desperately tried to stay afloat.

In March 1979, the vagabond and his dogs were seen outside the Seven Steps public house on Sefton Street, and this time he was causing a disruption with an enormous pack of dogs numbering at least thirty. The vagrant was moved on by the authorities without incident. In the 1980s they say the peculiar tramp was seen in the area around Copperas Hill, Seymour Street and Norton Street, and there is one report of him loitering near Lee's Butchers in the same area at that time.

And then the tramp died, supposedly from exposure after sleeping in a certain park one freezing wintry night. He was buried in Springwood cemetery, and they say his graveside was visited by gangs of stray dogs for quite a while afterwards. And then – well, this is where things take a supernatural twist, because there were multiple sightings of the supposedly deceased Dog Man for up to a year afterwards.

Alison Webb, who lived in a maisonette on Edge Hill's Smithdown Road, looked out of her window one evening, and there in the grounds of the old church of St Stephen, on Grove Street, was the Dog Man and his pack. Alison had heard that the tramp had died, and so was very puzzled by what she was seeing. The next moment the vagrant and his hounds slowly faded away. She was still trying to make sense of it all, when, a minute later, the telephone rang, startling her. It was her mother June, who lived less than two hundred yards away in Paddington. From the window of her flat, she too had seen the vanishing act and had rung her daughter to tell her about the strange spectacle.

Surely Alison and her mother had been mistaken? Surely it was simply a case of mistaken identity? After all, we live in a city of animal lovers, and perhaps someone, perhaps even another down-and-out, had taken to befriending and feeding the abandoned street dogs with butchers' bones; perhaps even as some gesture to carry on the Dog Man's work?

At 8pm, one February evening in 1980, a policeman came across the ghosts of the Dog Man and his canine retinue on Parr Street, in the city centre. The dogs were howling and snapping at each other, making such a racket that the constable, who had seen the dog-loving tramp on his beat many times over the years, decided he would have to intervene and order the vagrant to get control of his pack, but when he approached him, the ragged figure moved away and disappeared down a poorly-lit cul-de-sac called Slater Place. The policeman went in pursuit, but when he turned the corner there was no longer any sign of the Dog Man, or any of his strays. They had all vanished into thin air. Unable to accept what his eyes, and ears – for the howling and barking had all ceased – were telling him, the policeman searched every inch of the dead-end alleyway, and established that there wasn't a soul about in Slater Place.

As recently as 2009, a woman named Mia wrote to me to tell me how, one night in September 2008, at around 10.30pm, she had been walking from a pub on Dale Street with two girlfriends, on her way to a Chinese restaurant. The three girls were walking down Manchester Street, on the way to their destination, when they were alarmed to see the approaching figure of a man in a long dark coat and a beret, surrounded by an assortment of about twenty scruffy-looking dogs. Having a phobia of dogs, Mia let out a helpless little whimper, and had to be dragged by her friends until she had safely passed all the dogs, which on this occasion were strangely quiet. After they had passed the hounds, she dared to look back, and was puzzled but greatly relieved to see that the dogs and the man in the beret had vanished into thin air.

Is it possible that the Dog Man was one of those unfortunate alienated individuals termed by the callous as a 'freak of nature'? Whatever he was, he seems to have loved his only companions, the poor discarded dogs of the streets. If this seemingly golden-hearted man is now a ghost, along with his spectral hounds, then I hope they are content to follow their caring master in another world that is above cruelty and starvation.

Possession by a supernatural entity can be voluntary or involuntary, and can produce effects and behaviour of a negative or positive kind, depending, of course, on the nature of the thing possessing the host. The Catholic Church accepts that a person may be subjected to a positive possession by the Holy Ghost – the Third Person of the Blessed Trinity, who can bring comfort, strength, and tremendous confidence to a sinner and accomplish the salvation of all distressed souls.

Possession by evil spirits is recognised by almost every religion on Earth, and possession in itself is not always seen as an indication of the sinfulness of the person possessed, with some Christian religions postulating that for hidden reasons, God sometimes allows an innocent person to be visited by the violence of the Devil. Such possessed people are termed 'demoniacs' by the Catholic Church.

Possession can be centred upon a single person, or spirits may invade the bodies of several people, thousands even. The best-documented mass-possession case on record, took place at the Swiss village of Morzine, and the affair started in 1857 with 'the strange affliction' of a peasant girl. This so-called affliction caused the girl to climb trees like a squirrel, speak in tongues, writhe in agony, and laugh maniacally in a phenomenally loud voice. Three weeks after the girl became 'afflicted', over 2,000 of the villagers also became affected, and they too spoke in unknown languages, acted like animals, screeched profanities and cursed the Bible.

The French Emperor Louis-Napoléon dispatched three companies of soldiers to tackle the demonic disturbances, but the possessions continued unabated, even after armies of Catholic priests were drafted into Morzine. The mass possessions eventually died down in 1865 and although the incident has never been satisfactorily explained, most psychologists today would say it was all down to that umbrella term which is always wheeled out in such cases – 'mass hysteria'.

Locally, there have been many cases of terrifying possession right here in Liverpool. I talked to a couple of elderly priests many years ago, who they told me of the exorcism of two boys on Princes Avenue in the 1960s. The boys, whom I shall called John and Paul, were cousins, both aged twelve at the time.

During the summer school holidays, John, from Halewood, went to stay with Paul at his home on Princes Avenue, Toxteth. The boys slept in bunk beds, with John on the bottom bunk, and Paul on the top. One evening after they had gone to bed, Paul's widowed mother June, found her son and nephew drawing strange, frightening faces on the wall next to their bunks. Both of the faces, although drawn separately by each boy, looked exactly the same, as if they had been stamped on to the wallpaper.

June was furious. 'What d'you think you're playing at, Paul? You haven't scribbled on walls since you were two.

And you, John, I'm surprised at you. I don't know what your mother's going to say when she hears about this.'

Both boys just looked at her in sullen silence, refusing to speak.

'You're both going to scrub that wall tomorrow until there's not a sign of anything left on it. Do I make myself clear?'

The boys still refused to speak, and in exasperation June went out of the room muttering under her breath.

That same night, at around 11.30pm, June looked in on the boys to check they were asleep and not up to any more mischief. This time each of the boys was lying on the top of his covers, both in weird contorted postures, as if they had tied their arms and legs into knots. At some signal the boys quickly untangled themselves at the precise same time and involving the exact same movements. Then, with remarkable swiftness, they tied themselves into another limb-tangling pose. June had no idea what to make of it all, but watching it was very unpleasant, all the more so because the boys were apparently fast asleep.

June gently tried to wake her son, but he couldn't be roused from his sleep, and the same was true of Paul – both of them refused to wake up. Suspecting something evil had befallen them, June rang up a local priest for advice, and as soon as he set foot in the house the next day, John and Paul, who had been sitting quite normally at the breakfast table, suddenly stopped eating and began to scream in unison.

Within days, the priest had performed an exorcism in the bedroom where the boys had first manifested the odd behaviour. John vomited a copious amount of yellow foam, and a huge insect, similar to a millipede, with an abnormally large head, twisted and writhed as it crawled out of his mouth and vanished after it had fallen on to the floor. Slimey matter that was later identified as seaweed and feathers oozed out from under the pyjamas of the young victims, and the sound of a distant bell could be heard ringing in the house. Paul suddenly announced, 'The death-bell is ringing. Two people will die on Princes Avenue today!' This chilling prophecy came to pass. A girl was knocked over and killed on the avenue and her grandmother died of a heart attack after hearing of her death.

After a very prolonged exorcism that lasted over twenty four hours, both boys fell into a coma-type state of unconsciousness, and the shadow of a man carrying a huge cross – interpreted by the priests as Christ carrying his cross to Calvary – suddenly crossed the bedroom. The instant this apparition faded away, the possessed children awoke – simultaneously – and both of them could recall nothing of the past few days. The faces they had drawn on the walls quickly became covered with a thick black fungus, and June had to have the bedroom redecorated, and then mounted a crucifix on the wall next to the bunk bed. She forbade her nephew from staying over again and started to attend church with her son each Sunday. John and Paul eventually went on to lead normal lives.

~

In the early autumn of 1876, there was a terrible case of alleged possession, which ended in the cold-blooded murder of two young sisters in Great Crosby, and the subsequent manifestation of a demonic being. The Church authorities tried to hush the case up and even attempted to gag the local press. The main newspaper of that time was the *Liverpool Mercury*, and it did report some of the details, but then someone in power, who must have had a tremendous influence on the editor, seems to have stepped in and stifled further reports of this strange and uncanny story.

It all started at St Luke's Church, Leece Street, when thirteen-year-old Gertrude Morris, or Gertie, as she was called, was celebrating the harvest festival with her school class at the church. Something strange took place, but the witnesses of the incident – mostly children – were probably forbidden by the church authorities to discuss the details of what happened, even with their parents.

Something is said to have appeared inside the church at the end of the central aisle, in front of the altar. Several people, speaking years after the incident, claimed that the manifestation was of a terrifying being resembling a gargoyle. It scattered all of the fruit, vegetables and hampers that had been collected for the harvest festival. The church looked as if a bomb had hit it.

Two priests allegedly tackled the entity, and tried to exorcise it, and somehow, all of the children were successfully evacuated from the church – except for Gertie Morris, who had fainted – and when the demon, or whatever it was, returned from whence it had come, the teenager was left unconscious and quivering, prostrate on the floor, with her arms and legs spread out like the Scottish cross of St Andrew.

Nothing more is known with any certainty about the behaviour of Gertie Morris in the church that day, but when she returned home to her house in Fairholme Road, Great Crosby, the thirteen-year-old seemed to have undergone a dramatic change of character, and we come next to the curious case of the dancing poker.

When Gertie whistled, the poker in the fire-grate

would stand up and jump about on the hearth-stone. Now, it is possible that Gertie wasn't possessed by some evil spirit; she might have had that rare talent of telekinesis, which is the psychic ability to move objects at will. A person possessing this talent simply wills the object to move with his or her mind, and it does.

Nevertheless, Gertie's mother, forty-three-year-old widow, Agnes Morris, was known to be a very religious woman, and on 23 September 1876, she evidently decided that her daughter was possessed by a devil, and she also came to believe, for reasons unknown to us, that the evil influence had begun to spread from Gertie to her two sisters Ellen, aged eleven, Anna Catherine, aged nine, and two brothers – James aged eight, and Henry, who was six.

Rather than call in the parish priest to deal with the matter, Agnes decided on more drastic action, and at six o'clock in the morning, she took a revolver to the beds of the children and systematically tried to shoot each one of them. Three of the five children escaped, along with their governess, Mrs Sarah Ilbury, but Gertie was not so lucky. She died first, blasted in the head at point-blank range as she slept, followed by Ellen. Mrs Morris then tried to shoot herself twice in the head, but the first shot missed and the second bullet merely grazed her forehead.

PC Nosworthy was the first person to witness the carnage and told Mrs Morris she was being taken into custody. She asked if the two daughters she had hit were dead, and the policeman confirmed that they were. Mrs Morris sighed with satisfaction, saying that the children would now be safe in heaven and she wished she was with them. The youngest child, six-year-old Henry, was found to have a bullet lodged in his brain, but it was too deep to operate. A priest was praying at the child's bedside, when Henry suddenly sneezed, and the bullet shot into his nose, where a surgeon removed it with a pair of pincers. Miraculously, the child then made a full recovery.

Mrs Morris was tried at the Liverpool Assizes in December of that year, and the jury, after just a few minutes' deliberation, acquitted her on grounds of insanity, and his Lordship, Justice Lindley, directed that Agnes Morris should be detained at her Majesty's pleasure.

The first family to move into the house where the killing of the young Morris sisters had taken place heard phantom gunshots in the following year in the upper rooms, and at Halloween, the entire family saw the pathetic ghosts of Gertie and Ellen Morris, standing at the top of the stairs in their blood-soaked nightdresses, making moaning sounds as they reached out towards the terrified family members. The family fled the house, even though it was midnight, and had to stay at a neighbour's.

The house with the grisly reputation then lay unoccupied for months, until a brother and sister, both in their seventies, moved in, but they too moved out after only a week, when blood started dripping from the parlour ceiling on to the dining table, even though there was no blood to be found anywhere upstairs.

The Jones family, formerly of Aigburth, moved into the murder house in the 1880s, and had only settled in for a week when they were awakened in the wee small hours by a loud thudding sound, which rocked the house to its foundations. Geoffrey Jones, the head of the family, set out to investigate the source of the thuds, and discovered that they were coming from the attic. Armed with a poker and a candle, he went up to the attic, and found himself confronted with a being he would remember to his dying day.

Surrounded by a rosy aura, a tall horned creature, which looked as if it was made from grey slate, stood in the middle of the attic. Its eyes were jet black, and when it opened its fearsome-looking mouth full of long fangs, a powerful sulphurous stench wafted at Mr Jones, who reflexively lifted his arm, ready to strike the thing with the poker. The gargoyle-like being let out a deep throaty cry, and Mr Jones hurled the poker at it. The poker glanced off its left horn, producing sparks, because it was thrown with such energy.

Mr Jones then turned and ran downstairs to gather his family and leave the house immediately. The Jones family walked through a terrific downpour, with lightning streaking the skies that night until they reached the house of a priest. The priest was informed of the monstrosity in the attic but he could not be persuaded to venture into the house.

Other unwitting families who made the mistake of moving into the house on Fairholme Road were confronted by the same 'gargoyle' in the attic over the years, with the last encounter taking place about 1910, when a man named Abbot claimed he had seen the beast emerging from the attic wall surrounded by smoke.

I believe the house on Fairholme Road is still haunted, and I have talked to people who have lived at the house. All of those I interviewed said that at Halloween, when the barrier between the world of the living and the realm of the dead is said to be at its thinnest, a strange gloom pervades the house from attic to cellar. Three acts of suicide have been carried out there and all of these acts of self-destruction took place in the attic during the month of October.

If there is indeed a demon in the attic of that house in

Great Crosby, did it really possess thirteen-year-ol Gertie and afterwards manifest itself at St Luke's Church that autumn in 1876? Or did the possession take place in the church? And did Gertie bring the demon home to Fairholme Road? We will probably never know the answer to these intriguing questions.

A respected demonologist who has studied this case in some detail, believes the entity was one of the seventy-two demons catalogued in an ancient esoteric work called the *Lemegeton*, a book attributed to none other than King Solomon himself, a master magician as well as a monarch, who was said to command the seventy-two demons with a special ring that bore his seal.

So what is the name of the demon that has a predilection for appearing in the attic of the Great Crosby house? Well, to even print or utter its name is tantamount to invoking it, so I must not do so. But why should the nameless demon choose to haunt an attic of all places? Well, according to the demonologist, it is possible that a portal into our level of existence was opened on purpose, or by accident, during a séance, or through dabbling with a ouija board, and if this is the case, it reinforces my advice to stay well clear of the upturned glass, unless you have studied the occult in a serious manner and are ready on all levels to face the forces of good and evil.

THE CREATURES FROM THE BOOTLE CAVERNS

The following story unfolded in the spring of 1972, when thirteen-year-old Bootle lad Stan McWhinney decided to play truant, or 'sag off school' as they said in those days. Stan was something of a fire-bug, and on this day he was walking around aimlessly armed with a box of Pilot Matches in his pocket, wondering what he could set fire to next. He wandered the streets until he came to Derby Park, where he met a boy around his own age named Peter Barclay. Peter, with his high forehead, dark closely-cropped hair and big eyes, magnified by even bigger spectacles, was nicknamed 'Brains', because of his resemblance to the character from the *Thunderbirds* television series, but it in fact, it was a rather appropriate nickname, since Peter was a very intelligent lad.

When Stan encountered him in Derby Park, Peter was trying out a homemade go-cart, of the soap-box and bicycle wheel type that most of us tried to make in our younger days, only Peter's model had a motorbike battery powering it, and the engine of this superior machine was the electric motor from an old vacuum cleaner he'd found in an entry. As intelligent as Peter was, he was silly enough to allow Stan McWhinney to have a go on the electric cart. Stan assured Peter he wouldn't go very far, but he got carried away with the euphoria of driving a cart that could do fifteen miles per hour, and drove out of the park and ended up to the end of Merton Lane, chased all the way by Peter.

Stan apologised to Peter, and praised him, saying he was a genius to have made such a cart.

'That's nothing,' said Peter. 'I've got a boat as well.' And he invited Stan back to his house to see it.

'A boat?' said Stan, raising a sceptical eyebrow as he went into the old Victorian house. 'How come you've got a boat inside the house? I don't believe you.'

Peter ignored his scepticism and introduced Stan to his old grandmother, who was wheelchair bound. She immediately grabbed Peter by the arm and whispered something to him, looking very serious, and Peter put his mouth close to his grandmother's ear and shouted, 'Oh, it'll be alright, Gran. Don't worry.'

Peter's Gran was a bit hard of hearing, and, turning her best ear to her grandson, she asked, 'What was that, son?'

'Fish and chips,' Peter said, mocking his Gran's deafness, and showing off in front of Stan. Peter tilted his head sideways, gesturing for Stan to follow him, and led him into the kitchen, where he lit a candle at the gas stove. Peter then led Stan down into the cellar, which was flooded, like a lot of cellars in Bootle, because of the natural springs that exist under the town, but this cellar was more like a swimming pool, but full of filthy-looking black water. At the foot of the wooden cellar steps an old rowing boat was tethered, in the middle of which were two red metal-cased roadwork lanterns, of the type the old cocky-watchmen would sit by.

Peter lit the lamps with the candle, and told Stan to get in the boat. Stan had something of a phobia of deep water, and refused at first, but Peter promised he'd be alright, as he wasn't taking the boat very far. As soon as Stan got into the boat and sat down, Peter showed him how to row, and only then did Stan notice the archway in the far wall of the dark cellar. The lifeboat drifted under the archway and down a tunnel which echoed with the sounds of water lapping the walls and dripping from the vaulted ceiling. Stalactites hung down from what looked like the roof of a cave, and Stan started to panic, feeling he couldn't breathe. 'Let's go back, I can't swim, let's go back,' he said, but Peter told him to keep rowing, promising that he'd be fine. Stan looked back and saw only darkness – he couldn't even see the cellar archway anymore, and once again he told Peter they needed to turn the boat around.

'No, stop worrying, I've been down here loads of times,' Peter bragged.

At this, Stan clenched his fist and thumped Peter in the back. The thudding sound echoed in the sunless cavern, and Peter snapped, 'Stop it, you idiot! Do that again and I'll jump out the boat and swim back!'

Stan reluctantly carried on rowing and again tried to look back. Just then something hit him hard on the back of the head and almost knocked him out of the boat. It was a huge stalactite, hanging down from the ceiling like a giant icicle. The impact knocked over the lamps and one of them went out.

'You stupid nit!' Peter said, 'You nearly capsized us.'

Stan was close to tears by now, and, to make matters worse, the second lamp's flame spluttered, then went out, leaving the boys floating along on the underground lake in pitch blackness.

'Oh heck! I can't see where we're going now!' Peter said, also panicking.

Stan suddenly remembered the box of matches in his pocket, and quickly took them out and fumbled for a match, which he struck. There were about a dozen left in the box, and each lasted just under twenty seconds. At one point, after one of the matches had gone out, the boat hit the side of a wall and spun around in the darkness, disorienting the boys. Peter took off his shoe and looked at the compass built into the innersole; a novelty built into certain makes of Clark's shoes at the time. He reckoned, from the compass, that the boat was going in the right direction back to the cellar, but then something horrific happened.

By the feeble light of the match, Stan saw something in the water coming towards the boat – a V-formation of

63

sewer rats, all swimming with just their whiskery snouts above the waterline. Most of the rats passed by the boat, but one huge one scrambled aboard and scuttled across Stan's hand with its scratchy wet paws, before jumping back into the water.

Barely a minute had elapsed after that ordeal, when another terrifying incident took place. Something climbed on to the boat with a clattering sound, and by the match-light, Peter and Stan could that see it was a creature neither of them had seen before – a cross between a shrimp and a giant crab. It had black beady eyes on stalks, a claw with fierce-looking pincers, and long spindly legs of an anaemic pinkish colour – the same colour as the long wiry antennae that quivered as they roamed over Stan's hand and face. He screamed and kicked out at the weird aquatic creature, which he estimated to be about two feet across and four feet in length. Stan's kick sent the crab-like creature plummeting overboard, back into the water. But their troubles were not over yet, for an army of the ghastly crustaceans were scuttling about on the glistening walls of the cave like so many giant spiders.

Eventually, they spotted a faint glimmer of light, which heralded the archway of the cellar again, and the two foolish lads scrambled out of the boat and ran up the cellar steps.

Peter Barclay was severely reprimanded by his father, who saw the pair emerge from the cellar, ashen-faced. Peter's father, who was a civil servant, warned Stan not to talk about the subterranean lake to anyone, because he would get into trouble with the authorities. He said that there was enough pure water under Bootle to keep a community going in the event of a nuclear attack – even though Peter and Stan had seen the sewer rats swimming in that water and scores of those abominable creatures with the pincers and probing antennae.

Stan and Peter remained friends, until 1975, when Peter Barclay had to move from Bootle to live in Cheshire. Stan later researched the underground lake and discovered that it does in fact exist under Bootle, exactly where Peter Barclay's house stood, on Merton Road near Well Lane and Water Street. Some older people Stan talked to even recalled certain well-to-do individuals taking a motor-boat down into a cavern that once existed near the Bootle Tannery.

How true this is I cannot say. There are many rumoured lakes beneath the streets of Liverpool, and some of them have come to light in a most unexpected way. Take, for example, the lake under the original Cavern Club on Mathew Street, which was uncovered during excavations in 1982. The site agent and architect explored the 120-foot-long and 70-foot-wide lake, which was nearly ten feet deep in some parts. The mystery deepened when it was subsequently discovered that the lake had actually been man-made, possibly some time in the eighteenth century, but the reason behind the underground glorified swimming pool has not yet been fathomed (no pun intended).

Nobody could have suspected, all those years ago, that the Beatles, and many other Merseyside bands, were performing over a man-made lake, and had there been any significant subsidence in the most famous cellar club in the world, a tragedy that does not bear thinking about could have occurred, and the course of popular music would undoubtedly have suffered as a result.

BANSHEES

THE MOUNT PLEASANT BANSHEE

I have collected reports of banshees from every corner of Liverpool, and from every decade from Victorian times to the twenty-first century, and I have noted that there has been a rather high incidence of banshee reports centred round Mount Pleasant. Why this is so? I can't say. Could a single entity be responsible for all of these reports? Again, I'm not sure, yet something tells me that one banshee, presumably being an immortal supernatural being, could be behind all of the following reports.

On New Year's Day, 1869, a strange wailing sound was heard around 11pm on Mount Pleasant. Scores of people heard the terrible lamentations, including several members of the Gee family, who lived at Number 3 Court, Duckinfield Street, which runs between Brownlow Hill and Mount Pleasant. John Gee could hear nothing, but his wife felt very uneasy when she heard the sad sobbing sound, because she recalled the tales of banshees told to her by an Irish relative when she was a child, and they had stuck in her mind ever since. Mr Gee went and stood on his doorstep on this wintry first night of the year, smoking a pipe, and a passing neighbour – a young woman named Kate McDonnell – greeted him.

Gee nodded to her without taking his pipe out of his mouth, and Miss McDonnell, who was walking slowly over the ice-slicked pavement, suddenly halted and said, 'Is Mrs O'Leary in labour?'

Mrs O'Leary was a woman in her thirties who lived nearby with her seven children.

'How should I know?' Mr Gee asked, bluntly,

probably wondering why the girl had aimed such an unusual and inappropriate question at him.

'But can't you hear her terrible wailings?' Miss McDonnell asked, puzzled.

Gee listened. He heard nothing but a stray dog barking somewhere in the distance. Nothing more. 'Think you're hearing things, girl,' he said.

Young Kate, feeling offended by his rudeness, continued on her way home through the moonlit court. Ten minutes after this, another neighbour, Mary Finnegan, came into Number 3 Court with a strange tale to tell, if anyone would care to listen. She had just been returning from her sister's house, and as she came up Mount Pleasant, she heard a woman crying and howling near the Consumption Hospital. This woman had long white hair, and she wore a dark green shawl and a black frock that touched the floor. The crying stranger howled much louder than seemed humanly possible, and as Mary hurried on ahead of her, she took a quick glance back at her. By the light of the nearest lamp-post, Mary could see that the woman's face was a ghastly white, and her face was contorted with torment. Her mouth opened making an impossibly large 'O', as she let out a blood-curdling shriek, which sent Mary Finnegan panting in sheer terror up the slope of Mount Pleasant.

'It was a banshee and no mistake,' Mary Finnegan told John Gee, and the woman quickly made the sign of the cross, then paused for a moment, looking skywards. 'Can you hear her now?' she asked with a shudder. 'There it goes again.'

'No I cannot,' John Gee told her, and as Mary Finnegan hurried to her home, Gee went back into his house and slammed the door shut behind him, muttering under his breath, 'Flippin' hysterical women. I'm surrounded by 'em.'

On the following day, 2 January 1869. John Gee got himself into an altercation with a local man named Philip Monaghan when the discussion they were having over religion got heated. 'I am an Orangeman!' John Gee proudly announced, upon which Monaghan attacked him. The two men rolled about in a violent struggle in the middle of Duckinfield Street, and at some point Monaghan pulled out a knife and killed Gee outright.

Many believed that the strange wailing sound that had been heard so clearly the night before had come from a banshee warning of Gee's imminent bloody end. His neighbours and family recalled how he himself did not hear the unearthly lamentations and legend has it that he or she who does not hear the banshee's wail – whilst everyone else around them can plainly hear the cry of the Celtic harbinger – will be the one to die within three days.

~

Sometimes, though not often, the banshee warns of an impending death which can be avoided. The following case is unusual on two counts: not only does the banshee deliver such a warning, she is also seen in broad daylight. Once again, Mount Pleasant is the backdrop to this supernatural incident.

One summer evening in 1887, nineteen-year-old Lizzy Davidson of Pomona Street, off Mount Pleasant, went out for a stroll with her nine-month-old baby, Daisy, in her arms. Accompanying Lizzy on this balmy August evening was her twelve-year-old sister Maureen. Lizzy was rather fond of drink, and upon reaching the Brownlow Hill end of Mount Pleasant, she went into the Globe Inn for her usual three glasses of milk stout and a measure of rum, while Maureen sat on the pub step nursing the baby on her lap. 'The first glass is for thirst,' Lizzy Davidson would usually tell little Maureen, 'the second for nourishment, and the third for relaxation.' But she never specified what the excuse was for the shot of rum.

Dusk was slowly approaching, but the street lamps hadn't yet been lit, and Maureen could clearly see an odd woman coming up the thoroughfare from the direction of Ashton Street. The woman was dressed in a long black robe, which reminded Maureen of the habit worn by the Notre Dame nuns. The approaching woman also wore a black hood, which partially covered her head of white hair. Moments before, people had been milling about at the junction of Brownlow Hill and Mount Pleasant, but now an uneasy silence had descended on the street outside the pub, which had become unaccountably deserted, save for the baby-minder and little Daisy, who was fast asleep.

The woman in black paused outside the Globe Inn and looked down at Maureen. The girl was struck dumb, because her face was chalk-white, her eyes bloodshot, and tears streaked down her pallid cheeks. One of the tears dripped off her lantern jaw and landed on Daisy's face and as it did so it sent lachrymal droplets that, in turn, sprayed Maureen's face, and the girl shuddered at how ice-cold they were. Maureen immediately sensed there was something not of this world about the hideous woman, and when she let out a high-pitched howl, Maureen clutched Daisy, who was stirring from her slumbers, tightly to her chest. Maureen sprang to her feet and ran into the Globe. The pub landlady, Ellie Turner, watched the child with the babe in her arms come into the parlour, obviously distressed. She went to ask her what the matter was, when Lizzy hastily intervened, guiltily telling Mrs Turner that Maureen had only been minding the baby for a short while, just until she'd had a much-needed drink.

Maureen told her sister and the landlady about the woman in black outside and her icy tears. The description seemed to strike a chord with Mrs Turner, for she suddenly became very concerned.

'What woman?' Lizzy queried her sister's claim with a smile, 'I only left you for a minute, Maureen. Are you sure you're not making this up?' She moved towards the pub door, aiming to show that there was nothing untoward outside, but Mrs Turner's hand shot out and grabbed the teenager by the forearm. 'Don't go out there!' she cried, a spasm of anguish playing across her face.

Lizzy returned a surprised look, 'Why ever not, ma'am?'

'Is the baby in good health?' Mrs Turner asked, studying Daisy's huge eyes as they fixed yearningly on Lizzy.

'Yes, she's a bonny baby,' Lizzy told the landlady, 'but why do you ask?'

Mrs Turner took Lizzy and her young sister into the hallway to afford them some privacy, and told them of her grave suspicions. 'You two get home now with that child, because that woman who passed by outside before was an eldritch.'

Maureen's mouth formed a perfect hollow circle as she listened, enthralled.

'What's one of those?' asked Lizzy.

'A banshee,' whispered Mrs Turner, and this time, Maureen and Lizzy understood perfectly what the landlady was referring to. Suddenly, the door in the hallway burst open, startling the Davidson sisters, and an old hunchbacked woman in black, with a plum-coloured shawl, came out of the parlour, bringing the hubbub of the drinkers and their mingled tobacco smoke with her. The door closed as the old woman stood there, her pale blue eyes darting between the sisters, the baby and Mrs Turner. 'Are they the nieces you were telling me about, Ellie?' Mrs Mooney asked the landlady.

'No, Eileen,' Mrs Turner replied, and she leaned forward and whispered something into the old woman's right ear, to which Mrs Mooney recoiled with a harsh contortion of her wrinkled features. 'No! Oh no!' she cried out in alarm.

'Get the baby home and keep her warm and fed,' Mrs Mooney suddenly advised Lizzy, and Mrs Turner gave energetic knowing nods at each word of her advice.

Lizzy's heart pounded with anxiety as she took Daisy out of Maureen's arms and left the Globe Inn. She hurried off for the crumbling house on Pomona Street, and every step of the way was punctuated with questions from Maureen. 'What's an eldritch, Lizzy? Was that a banshee I saw? Is Baby going to die?'

Daisy was doted on that night by Lizzy, her older sister Mary Jane, their mother, and even the grandmother Margaret, who assured everyone that Maureen had not met a banshee outside the Globe Inn; why, it had, in all probability, only been 'Mad Madge', a demented widow from Shaw Street. Lizzy felt this explanation didn't ring true somehow and could take no comfort from it, but never told anyone of her fears.

The night passed without incident, but on the following morning, at 10pm, Lizzy was serving at a tobacconist's on Mount Pleasant, when Maureen ran into the shop in floods of tears. The girl was so distraught, she couldn't get her words out, and Lizzy, somehow sensing that something awful had happened to Daisy, rushed out from behind the counter and shook her young sister by the shoulders. 'Has something happened to Daisy? Tell me! Why are you crying? Is Daisy alright?'

Maureen nodded repeatedly as she sobbed, then managed to say, 'Something's happened.'

Within a few minutes the two sisters arrived home, and there in the back yard, in the early morning sunshine, Daisy lay in her cot, which Maureen had brought outside on this fine summer's day. The child was smothered from head to toe in a swarm of noisy wasps.

Lizzy approached her baby in shock, and Maureen told her how some boys had been sitting on the back yard wall, arguing over a large jar of malt (which one of them had most probably stolen). One of the boys snatched the jar off the other and began scooping handfuls of the brown syrupy contents into his mouth. Another boy then snatched the jar back off him, plunging his hand into the malt to take a scoop, which he then playfully threw at his friend. The globule of malt missed its intended target and landed instead on Daisy in her cot. Maureen shouted at the boys, and they jumped down off the wall. Maureen went to fetch a wet flannel and a towel to clean Daisy, but had found her coated with wasps when she returned.

Lizzy screamed out in pain as two wasps circled her and then stung her and Maureen cried out for her grandmother, but she had left the house to go to the market. Maureen ran outside and called to a policeman. PC 563 Farrar was on his beat on Mount Pleasant when he saw the hysterical girl and ran to her aid. He somehow managed to pick up Daisy and gently shoo away the wasps, extracting two from the baby's mouth, without the infant being stung, although he himself was stung twice.

Lizzy thanked PC Farrar and hugged Daisy, who was in tears with all of the commotion. Only later that day did Maureen remind her big sister about the alleged banshee who had seemingly cried over Daisy on the previous evening. From that moment on, Lizzy became a devoted mother to Daisy, attending to her every need and only rarely squandered her money and time on drink.

~

Number 64 Mount Pleasant is a Georgian town house, built in 1773, and until recently, it was a registry office. In August 1962, John Lennon married his first wife, Cynthia Lennon, at this address, but sixty-eight years before, in 1894, Number 64 was the home of the Rose family. Frederick Rose, the head of the family, was a well-known and respected dentist, and in the October of 1894, something very strange took place at Number 64, which has never been explained.

It all began on the Tuesday evening of 9 October 1894, at 11.15pm, when the loud mournful cries of a woman were heard heard on Mount Pleasant, outside of Number 64. A Dr Crawford, who lived in the house facing Number 64, went to his window upon hearing the strange crying, which began low, then rose to a high-pitched crescendo. The physician saw a tall hooded woman in black walking slowly past Number 64, going in the direction of the YMCA. At midnight, the crying woman returned, and once again Dr Crawford went to his window. He saw the second floor window of Number

64 lift open, and a man look out. He then emptied what looked like a chamber pot on to the late-night wailer, thoroughly soaking her. The doctor was disgusted by this behaviour – what a despicable thing to do – but it seemed to have an effect; the woman ceased crying and walked slowly away with her head bowed, towards Roscoe Street, where she vanished into the darkness.

On the following morning, Dr Crawford left his home to visit a friend, and on Mount Pleasant he saw thirty-four-year-old William Muir, the butler of the Rose household at Number 64, and the doctor recognised him as the man who had doused the sobbing woman with the chamber pot. Crawford had words with Muir about the disgraceful act of the night before, and the butler explained that he had resorted to such action because Mrs Rose, his employer's wife, had been alarmed by the crying lady, whom she believed to be a banshee. Muir had shouted to the deranged woman, telling her to go away from the street, but she had taken no notice, and instead had continued her mournful parade up and down outside the house.

A few days later, on the morning of Thursday, 11 October, at 9am, there was a terrific explosion at Number 64 Mount Pleasant. Dr Crawford ran to the window and looked across the road at a terrible scene. Smoke was pouring out of the room above the dental surgery at Number 64, and the butler, William Muir, was on fire. He used his fists to punch the panes of glass out of the window, then crashed through the window frame, his body ablaze, and fell to the pavement below with a dull thud. Dr Crawford grabbed his Gladstone bag and ran across the road from his surgery to administer aid to the butler, but a group of men had already moved him to the hotel next door. Crawford heard Muir saying he had smelt gas at the house, and had lit a piece of paper to a dark spot in the house where he believed the gas to be escaping. The butler then passed out from shock. He was taken to the Southern Hospital, where he sadly died without regaining consciousness. He had sustained burns and broken ribs in the fall but the coroner determined that it was shock that had killed him. The butler was described afterwards as a sober and very reliable man.

Expert gasfitter, Davidson Carr, was sent to inspect the damaged house, to determine if a gas leak had caused the explosion, but Carr stated that, despite undertaking a thorough search of the house, he could not find any evidence of any gas leakage. All the pipes were perfectly tight, and Carr, and several other gasfitters who subsequently investigated the accident, were unable to account for the explosion that killed William Muir.

Frederick Rose, the butler's employer, told police he had been in his bath when he heard the explosion, and had quickly put on a dressing gown and told his family to get out of the house, at which they all ran out into the street with several servants. They had all then seen the poor butler lying on the pavement with flames issuing from his clothes.

That night, the servants of the Rose household talked in hushed voices below stairs about the strange crying woman who had walked up and down outside the house on the evening before the tragedy, and one of the servants said she was in no doubt that the mourner in question had been a banshee, for William Muir's mother had been Irish.

~

Moving forward through time, to March 1966, we come to the kitchen of the YMCA on Mount Pleasant, where a group of female kitchen staff are getting ready to divest themselves of their blue overalls and leave for home after a hard day's slog cooking meals, washing dishes and serving the students at the 'YM, as it was affectionately nicknamed in those days.

At 10pm, six women left the staffroom and walked out into the breezy night air on to a bustling Mount Pleasant. One of the women, thirty-six-year-old Mary, cupped her hand around a friend's lighter, and after three attempts in the March wind, managed to light her cigarette. She then bid her colleagues goodnight as she reached the entrance to Roscoe Street, a poorly-lit narrow street in those times. Mary was joined by her workmate Joan, who, like Mary, also lived in Toxteth. Joan shouted goodnight to her four workmates, then turned the corner and strolled down Roscoe Street, chatting with Mary and discussing the bits of gossip she had picked up in the kitchens during her gruelling work-shift, which had stretched today from noon till 10pm.

As the women passed the junction with Oldham Street, they both heard a low-pitched howling sound which rapidly rose in both volume and pitch, almost like a siren, except the two startled women could hear what sounded like words in an unknown language amidst the dreadful cacophony. Then they saw the source of the din.

In a dim corner of Oldham Street, there stood a woman with long white hair which hung down from beneath a black hood. Her robe, which touched the pavement, was almost as dark as the hood, and a pale face could just be seen inside the hood, with two dark socket-like eyes. The mouth in this ashen face opened

78

wide, and the ululation that followed, chilled the blood of the two female onlookers. A sound reminiscent of a gale-force wind howling through bare-branched trees filled Roscoe Street.

Mary and Joan turned on their heels and ran towards the well-lit thoroughfare of Leece Street, where they could still hear the woman crying. The two kitchen workers clung on to one another as they crossed Leece Street and headed for Berry Street, and it was a while before Mary finally said, 'Oh my God! You don't think she was a banshee, do you?'

'That's just what I was thinking,' Joan agreed.

'Oh my God, Joan! Doesn't that mean someone in your family's going to die if you see one of them?'

Joan thought back to the things her grandmother had told her about the banshee. She squeezed Mary's upper arm as she recalled her grandmother's warning, 'The wail of the banshee usually means someone in the family of the person who has heard it will soon be dead.'

'Crikey!' said Mary, 'I hope it isn't me mum ... she's been really bad with her stomach the past week.'

'Just make sure you say a prayer when you get home, Mary,' Joan suggested, 'God's stronger than evil.'

On the following day, Mary got the shock of her life when she was told that her cousin Kevin had been found dead in a yard in Oldham Street – the very street where Mary and Joan had encountered the banshee. Kevin was the black sheep of his family, and had lived a life of crime until, at the young age of twenty-six, he had fallen from a ladder he was using in an attempt to break into a house in Oldham Street. He had fallen just fifteen feet, but had cracked his head on a stone window-ledge as he fell, breaking his neck. The coroner said Kevin had not died immediately, but had lain in the cold pitch-black yard for about an hour until he had died from his injuries. Unable to move, he had drowned in his own blood, which had trickled from the internal injuries into his throat, clogging up his lungs.

Kevin had fallen from the top of the ladder at around 9.30pm, and would have been lying in the yard, slowly dying as his cousin Mary had passed by unaware of his plight. Mary and Kevin had the same Irish surname, and I have traced their ancestral roots back to a village near Cork. Mary's mother later admitted that she had heard an inexplicable wailing sound in her bedroom three years before – an hour before the news of President John F Kennedy's assassination broke. The Kennedy clan, incidentally, are said to have been haunted by a banshee for generations, and this banshee is said to have been seen and heard near to the White House in July 1999 when John F Kennedy Junior died in a plane crash.

~

It might be a cliche, but Liverpool really is an ethnic melting pot, and most of the people have a touch of the Celtic in their DNA, which can connect them to the banshee. A case in point is a black man named Robert who lived in Edge Hill in the 1970s. Robert had a Jamaican father, and for many years he never knew that his mother, Philomena, was Irish. Philomena had come over from County Monaghan in the 1950s and had lived with Robert's father on Upper Parliament Street for years. Two years after Robert was born, Philomena split with her husband and went to live in the United States, leaving Robert with his father. Robert often asked about his mum, but his father would tell him nothing.

In 1970, Robert's father passed away and the boy went to stay with his aunt Hilda in the St Andrew's tenements (also known as the Bull Ring), off Brownlow Hill.

One evening in 1972, when Robert was twelve, his cousins took him to the Silver Blades Ice Rink in Kensington. He was a natural skater, and enjoyed his time at the ice rink, but later that evening, as he and his cousins were going home, they were accosted by the eerie sounds of a woman crying hysterically. At first they thought the cries were coming from someone on Prescot Road, but Robert and his three female cousins soon realised, to their horror, that the unseen wailing woman was actually following them.

At one point the invisible mourner fell quiet, but when the four young people reached Brownlow Hill, she resumed her wailing with a vengeance. By now, other people passing by could also hear the distressing sounds, which seemed to be hanging in the air. The spectral sobbing continued until Robert and his cousin reached the door of Aunt Hilda's flat. It then ceased abruptly, and when Robert and his cousins told their aunt about the ghostly crying, she thought they were just imagining it.

A week later, a grey-haired woman called at Hilda's home in the Bull Ring. She was Kathleen, the older sister of Robert's Irish mother. She had traced Hilda and her nephew after making various enquiries, and had come bearing bad news. Robert's mother had died a week ago in New York in a car crash. When allowances had been made for the five-hour time difference between New York and Liverpool, it was discovered that Philomena had died at the very hour that Robert and his cousins had heard the strange wailing sounds upon leaving the Silver

Blades Ice Rink. Kathleen believed it was the family banshee that John and his cousins had heard, for she herself had heard it when her sister died, and she had heard it twice before when other members of the family were about to pass away.

THE GREEN GIRL OF EVERTON ROAD

If ever there was a sister to the Banshee, it was the Green Girl of Everton Road, who has been seen by people from all walks of life since Victorian times. She is also said to be a harbinger of death, particularly of babies and the young.

In early December 1972, twelve-year-old Michael Williams was sitting in the parlour of his Everton home on Breck Road, trying to make a bow and arrow out of a knitting needle, a plastic coat hanger, and an elastic band, which unfortunately snapped and stung his knuckle. The boy had just been watching an exciting television serial called *The Black Arrow* based on Robert Louis Stevenson's 1888 novel, and Michael had decided he wanted to take revenge on a school bully who'd given his younger brother a nasty dig a week back. He actually intended to unleash a hail of arrows at this bully, but fortunately, Michael's mum Margy put paid to his vengeful plans, when she suddenly asked him to go and drop off some money to his older sister Glynis, who lived on Hall Lane in Kensington.

Michael complained that he was too tired, and so his mum called him 'an ornament' and had to give him a few bob for sweet money in order to induce him to go on the errand. All the way up Breck Road ran Michael, whistling the theme tune to the Black Arrow, and with his imaginary bow, he shot off make-believe arrows at different people until he got to the shop, where he bought Bazooka Joe chewing gum and a bag of toffee bonbons, coated in a fine dusting of violet sherbet. The time was around 7pm, and being December, it was already dark. Michael was only too glad to reach his sister's home in Kensington, and as usual, she and her husband Terry, made a fuss of him. The boy's sister was heavily pregnant, and yet she still made him something to eat, gave him cream soda and apple pie, all of which encouraged him to overstay his welcome. He didn't realise how late it was until he saw *New at Ten* starting on the television.

He set off for home at once, and as he was walking briskly up Everton Road, he thought he heard a woman crying somewhere in the distance. The strange sound really unnerved him. A quick look around quickly told him there wasn't a soul about. There was the crying sound again, and this time it seemed to be coming from somewhere by the vicarage. Michael started to whistle the theme tune to the *Black Arrow* television serial to bolster up his courage, and tried to imagine he was one of the Black Arrow outlaws of old, but then, all of a sudden, something behind him lit up. A faint green glow illuminated the pavement in front of him. The lad turned around to be met by a terrifying sight.

A girl of about sixteen or seventeen stood there in her bare feet, cradling a baby in her arms. She and the baby were giving off a soft green light, and the girl's long hair was blowing about in the winter breeze. Her clothes were poor and ragged and seemed to shimmer in the green light. The girl opened her mouth and let out the most heart-stopping wail. The baby looked as if it was very ill, or even worse. The girl cried out in a language Michael had never heard before, and then held the poor child out towards him.

Michael turned on his heels and ran off as fast as his legs could carry him – all the way to his house on Breck Road. The first thing his mother greeted him with was, 'Where the hell have you been, you gallivanter? You've had me worried sick.'

Michael ran straight past her to the cold water tap in the kitchen and gulped a great mouthful from it, even though his mother had repeatedly told him it was a disgusting 'common' habit. Only then was he able to stammer out a description of his encounter with the glowing ghost of the girl and her baby. Michael's mother didn't believe him, and warned him about telling fibs, saying liars went mad in the end because they finished up believing their own lies. She even said she could see the tell-tale black spot on his tongue – the mark of a liar.

Michael's grandmother Gladys, was sitting in the corner, watching the horror series *An Appointment With Fear*, and when she overheard her grandson mention the green glowing girl of Everton Road, she turned down the volume on the television before hurriedly making the sign of the cross. She shot a terrible sombre expression to her daughter Margy – Michael's mum. Margy read the worried expression and said, 'What's up, Mam? Why've you switched off the telly?'

Grandma Gladys threw her hands to her face. 'Oh Lord! Please no!' she gasped. She explained that the ghost Michael had encountered had been seen many times before on Everton Road. 'Was it by the vicarage?' she asked.

'What's a vicarage?' Michael asked, and his Gran described the old-looking building. Michael nodded. Gladys said whenever that ghost of the young girl and her baby was seen, it meant anyone pregnant in the family would lose their baby.

'Oh shut up, Mam, with your daft superstitions. You'll terrify our Michael,' said Margy, but the expression on her face betrayed her own fears, as she added, 'Our Glynis is having a baby.'

'As true as we're all sitting here, love,' Gladys told her daughter, 'that ghost has been seen for years, and I'm going way back to when my mother saw her ... always by the vicarage.'

'Mam, you'd better shut up, I don't want to hear any more,' Margy snapped, and pointing her finger right in Michael's face she said, 'He hasn't seen anything; he's just come up with all this because he was out roamin' till all hours. You can get to the bottom of a thief but you can never get to the bottom of a liar.'

'I'm not lyin', Mam,' Michael again protested. And then he suddenly recalled something, 'Hey, Gran, you know what she said, that ghost?'

Michael's Gran was all ears. 'Go on, lad, I believe you; I know you're telling the truth because you've gone all goosepimply.'

Michael tried to recall the exact words the ghost had said. He seemed to be speaking gibberish as he gave his approximation of the only phrase he could remember.

His grandmother went cold, because she knew a little Gaelic, with her father being Irish. And she recognised the admirable attempt Michael had made at mimicking the spectre's remark. Without a doubt, the phrase Michael had heard was a Gaelic one that translated meant, 'Never to be'.

That night, just after twelve o'clock, a Mrs Shaw, a former neighbour of the Williams family, who now lived in Kensington, called at the house with her two daughters. As soon as Margy Williams opened the door,

Mrs Shaw's two beautiful but burly-looking daughters seized her, with their hands on her shoulders and waist, and led her to her own kitchen. 'What's going on?' Margy asked, her face pale and grim with expectation. 'Oh my god! It's Glynis isn't it? It's the baby isn't it?'

Margy threw her hands up to her face and looked at the harbingers through splayed fingers.

Mrs Shaw put the kettle on and made the tea extra sweet, because it would help treat the shock. Margy wouldn't drink it. Mrs Shaw got her daughters to sit Margy down in the kitchen, and then she broke the dreadful news. Glynis had lost her baby and was now in the Royal Infirmary, after suffering a severe haemorrhage.

So it was true then. The green girl had been wailing for her daughter's poor dead baby. Margy's mournful crying that night made poor Michael run upstairs and hide under the covers, for it was as though the green girl had brought all her terrible sadness into the house.

Fortunately, Glynis pulled through, and two years later, she gave birth to a healthy boy.

The identity of the ghost on Everton Road is still unknown, but she certainly speaks Gaelic, and she's probably one of the thousands of Irish people who came to this city to escape the Great Famine.

When I mentioned the Green Girl on the *Billy Butler Show*, in 2010, the telephone switchboard went haywire with calls from listeners who had either seen or heard about the apparition, and Billy was inundated with emails from listeners at home and abroad. My own grandmother, Rose Slemen, once told me how her aunt had seen the Green Girl the day before her brother was killed in the First World War. My great-grandmother Bridget O'Donnell had also seen her the day before her twin sisters both died in a fire.

A woman named Kathy, who afterwards lost most of her family in the May Blitz, accidentally ran straight through the ghost one evening when she was playing on Everton Road as a child during the Second World War. Why the Green Girl haunts Everton Road is not known, but I will continue to research this intriguing but sad apparition, so I can hopefully throw further light on her behaviour. I feel there is a tragic story to tell regarding the poor long-dead teenager, and, perhaps when it finally comes to light, and she is properly identified, she will finally rest in peace.

THE MAIDENS OF THANATOS

The banshee is but one species of death-harbinger that exist within a wider genus of supernatural maidens, ranging from the Fates, of Greek and Roman mythology, to the modern fatally-unlucky entities that I term the Maidens of Thanatos, the Greek god of death. In Ancient Greece, the Fates were called the Moirai, and in Latin they were known as Fatae. In our folkore the Fates were called the Harsh Spinners, the Daughters of the Night, and were traditionally depicted as three women in black who controlled and dictated the destiny of every man, woman and child. Their names were Clotho, who spun the thread of life, Lachesis, who measured it (determining how long a life should be), and Artropos, who cut it (thus ending that life).

These Maidens of Death are found in every culture across the world, and are reminiscent of the Hindu goddess Kali (the deity from which Calcutta derives its name), who symbolises death, destruction and bloodthirstiness. Red-eyed Kali is depicted as wearing earrings of corpses, a necklace of skulls, and her idol was often besmeared with the blood of victims sacrificed to her by the members of the Thugs cult.

The female is an archetype of the Great Mother, who gives birth to mankind, but there is a flip-side to the loving, nurturing archetype, which stretches back in time to Lilith, the Queen of the Night, who was Adam's first wife (before Eve) in the Jewish Talmud. Lilith refused to lie beneath Adam during intercourse, insisting that she was his equal. In the end she uttered the highly-dangerous full name of God, then 'flew off into the air' to leave Adam for Lucifer.

Over the millennia, the occultists have maintained that Lilith, now a very superior demon, has often been responsible for the much-reported midnight seduction of males over the centuries. Such sexual assaults are also said to be the work of shadowy supernatural maidens known as the Succubi. These are beautiful women who have a sinister agenda in their nocturnal attacks on men.

The Maidens of Thanatos are still around today, and here are just a few stories that tell of their grim work.

First a friend saw her, but I argued the thing was possibly a mirage on the beach, and then one of my relatives saw her, and I blamed it on a trick of the light, but then in 1989 I saw her for myself – a startling apparition of a woman in black upon Formby Sands.

She stood among the windswept dunes with the seaborne breezes stirring her long black hair, and through a pair of binoculars borrowed from a bird-watching colleague, I was able to study the ghost's deathly face, as pale and lifeless as the marble countenance of a statue. Her eyes were black as ink, and her mouth seemed to be opening slowly. By her side I saw the huge black hounds – the legendary Dogs of Death, known as strakers – and at once I realised this was the fabled wraith of the Death Maiden with her hounds of Hell, whose appearance foretells the end of a life in the near future. I chose to look away upon this stormy late afternoon in September, but my friend grabbed his binoculars back, and although I warned him not to look at the ghost, he zoomed in on the stark black figure.

'Come on, let's go ... come on!' I urged him, but curiosity had got the better of him. All of a sudden, he said, 'The size of those dogs! Wait a minute! They're coming this way!' And then we were running for dear life for the car, the baying of the 'Moggan Tar', as the Gaelic call these Death Dogs, ringing in our ears. They are also known as the gytrash, and a dozen other names in tongues of Gaelic, Saxon and mongrel English.

All the way back to Liverpool, through the greyness of the dying day, we could hear the distant howls and barks of the hunting pack, even though we were inside the car, and they could still be faintly heard after we had put several miles between ourselves and them.

Within just two days, my friend was dead from an undiagnosed heart defect, and in his last hour he told nurses that he could hear dogs at the side of his hospital bed.

~

In 1920, the maiden of death had been sighted with her pack of black dogs on the eve of the infamous Formby Sands Murder. She stood on the top of the ancient wind-whipped dunes, where the sea and the land have fought wars of erosion for thousands of years. Once, in the remote past, a vast forest stretched from the sands across to Wirral, and petrified stone tree trunks can still be found beneath the waters and the sandstone strata, the vestiges of this ancient green domain and of an unknown nature-worshipping people. If you know where to look, you may see the withered stone trunks of the vanished forest at unusually low tides at Hightown and Leasowe.

In March 1920, the ominous spectre was seen by two lovers – former soldier Herbert Salisbury and divorcee Alice Pearson – who had come to Formby sands to die together in a suicide pact. Salisbury shot Alice to death with a revolver, then turned the gun on himself with a shaking hand, but couldn't go through with it. He ran to a local pub with the eerie howls still reverberating in his ears.

At the ensuing court case, Mr Justice McCardle believed the ex-soldier to be obviously of unsound mind, but Herbert Salisbury pleaded guilty to his lover's murder and said he wanted to join her in eternity. The judge refused the prisoner's plea, but the police surgeon decided that the soldier was sane; that the 'delusions' were only drink-induced, and so he was hanged in the month of May 1920, at Walton Gaol. His death-wish had finally been fulfilled.

~

In Northumberland Street, Toxteth, in 1978, a woman named Betty visited the terraced house of her friend Rita. It was her first visit to the house, and although the dwelling was small compared to Betty's house in Tuebrook, she thought the place was really cosy. Betty was amazed at the way Rita would, like many people in the street, leave her front door ajar without any worries; something you're not likely to see today today in our crime-ridden society. Even then, Betty advised Rita to keep her front door shut, as there were plenty of rogues about, even amongst the close-knit community of 'Northummy' (as Northumberland Street was nicknamed by the locals).

On the second visit to Rita's home, in the late summer of 1978, Betty called at the house at around 7pm and again found the door ajar. She knocked then called out Rita's name, before walking in. It had been four months since Betty had last paid a visit, and she thought Rita had had the place decorated and altered, for this time she was surprised and rather embarrassed, to see Rita's fuzzy outline through the frosted glass shower cubicle. 'Oh dear!' Betty gasped, and hid her smile with her hand. 'I didn't know you were having a shower ... sorry,' she said. But Rita didn't seem to hear her with the noise of the shower, or perhaps she had water in her ears!

Betty sat herself down and started watching the television, which was switched on in the corner of the room, and suddenly she had the unsettling feeling that she was being watched. She looked to her right, and there in the corner of the living room was a girl of about fifteen with long reddish brown hair, parted in the middle, and an almost milk-white complexion mottled with freckles. Her eyes were a vivid amber-brown, and she was wearing a dark-grey school uniform consisting of a cardigan, shirt and skirt. Betty surmised that the schoolgirl was some relative of Rita's, possibly a niece, and she smiled at her, but she did not react.

Betty then noticed that dark red liquid was flowing from the corners of the girl's mouth and was dripping down her chin, neck and into her school shirt, though she didn't seem to notice. Betty was horrified, and leapt to her feet to go to the girl's aid, thinking she must have seriously injured herself, but the haemorrhaging suddenly became even worse, and blood gushed out of the girl's mouth, which had now curved into a sinister smile.

Betty cried out in alarm, at which the red-haired girl vanished instantly. Betty stumbled towards the front door and crossed the threshold back into Northumberland Street, and suddenly noticed Rita on the other side of the road standing on her doorstep, obviously looking out for her. Betty realised she must have gone to the wrong house, and hurried across the road. 'Where've you been?' said Rita. 'It's half-past seven.'

Betty stammered out her account of how she had gone to the wrong house, and how she had seen the solid-looking ghost of a schoolgirl who had vanished before her eyes after haemorrhaging at the mouth. Rita could see Betty looked rather shaken by her experience, and brought her into the house and sat her down while her daughter made her a strong cup of tea.

Rita told Betty that the house she had mistakenly walked into belonged to a former neighbour named Tina, who had the reputation of being something of a loose woman. She had been divorced by her husband because he was sick of the affairs she was continually having with men half her age. Tina had no children, so Rita was baffled by the ghost of the schoolgirl that Betty described. However, Tina had only lived at the house for two years, so Rita assumed it was possible that she hadn't encountered the macabre apparition herself.

Three days after Betty had seen the ghost, Rita's fifteen-year-old son Michael was awakened at 1.20am by the sensation of someone sitting on his bed. He opened his eyes to find a long-haired female figure sitting on the right side of his bed. He turned on the bedside lamp and saw it was a red-haired girl in a school uniform. Her face was very pale and freckly, and her eyes were dark and so sad-looking.

'Who are you?' Michael asked, sitting bolt upright, and as before, when Betty had encountered the ghost, the girl's mouth started to ooze blood. Michael tossed back the duvet and ran out of the room with the ghost in close pursuit. She laughed as she chased him, and the ghastly blood sprayed out as she opened her mouth. Michael ran into his parents' room and roused them. Both parents watched, with a trembling Michael between them, as the handle of their bedroom door slowly turned.

'Who's there?' Michael's father called out. He took quick nervous breaths as the door steadily opened to reveal – nothing. There was nobody there.

Days after this, another bizarre incident took place.

Michael was drinking a glass of cola one afternoon, when he suddenly had a strong irrational impulse to bite the lip of the tumbler. His teeth crunched through the glass, and he screamed as blood poured from his badly-cut lips and gums. Rita became hysterical as she tried unsuccessfully to stop the bleeding with a towel, and Michael lost so much blood, he had to be given a transfusion.

That same week, Betty visited her dentist to have a filling in a large back molar, but the dentist's drill somehow slipped, and hit a large vein in her gum. Although Betty's mouth was numb to pain, she could feel the warm blood gushing out of the terrible wound and pouring down her throat, making her choke. Betty was taken to hospital when the bloodflow couldn't be stemmed, and received four stitches in her gum. These two gruesome accidents, which led to bloodletting in the mouth have, in my opinion, an eerie parallel with the ghostly blood-slobbering schoolgirl who was seen by Michael and Betty.

It is said that the teenaged phantom was seen in quite a few other Northumberland Street bedrooms, usually in the dead of night, and her bedside manner was always the same. The blood would pour from her mouth, and she would follow or chase the frightened victim (usually someone in their teens) for a short distance before vanishing away. Then an awful event would befall the family, and in some cases there are reports of sudden, bizarre deaths following the hauntings.

What is the story behind the nocturnal red-haired frightener? One woman I talked to believes she is the ghost of a girl who suffered a brain haemorrhage in the street in the 1960s, and died with blood streaming from her mouth. Thankfully, for the people in Northumberland

Street, the ghost has not done her rounds in the bedrooms in recent years, although ghosts of this sort can often come out of the woodwork again without warning …

~

At a house in Lark Lane, a creepy woman in black, who looks as if she dates back to Edwardian times, has a habit of ripping the bedsheets off people trying to enjoy a good night's sleep, and worse still, those to whom she appears soon hear of a death within their circle of family or friends. Sometimes, the entity even resorts to trying to smother the sleepers with a pillowcase.

The house in question had been haunted by this dangerous entity for over fifty years when I first investigated the incidents in the 1990s. When the house was sold and divided into flats, the new owners were not aware of the invisible permanent resident on their premises, but the first tenant to move in, a plumber by the name of Jackson, soon came face to face with this particularly nasty ghost.

He was awakened at around 3am by the ticklish sensation of someone feeling his toes. He looked over the covers but there was nobody about. Dismissing the sensation as the product of a realistic dream, he turned over, snuggled down and tried to get back to sleep, but then he felt a distinct tugging at his duvet from behind. A cold clammy hand touched his back, and immediately he was wide awake, full of adrenalin. When he looked back on the incident he was surprised by his quick response to the invasion, fabricating a lie designed to scare off the bedroom intruder, 'I've got a gun under my pillow,' he had threatened.

Mr Jackson really did think a burglar had got into his bedroom, especially since, at the time, there had been reports in the *Liverpool Echo* of a spate of burglaries on Lark Lane.

The next thing a small hand slid over his shoulder; unmistakably a woman's gloved hand. Mr Jackson screamed out a profanity and rolled sideways out of the bed and on to the floor. When he looked up, the tall silhouette of a woman in a huge feathered hat was towering above him. She started to chuckle and said something the plumber couldn't quite make out. He scrambled to his feet, and in nothing but his Y-fronts, fled from his flat and down the communal staircase. He refused to go back into the flat until dawn was breaking.

On the following day, he received some terrible news. His much younger brother had been knocked over and killed by a drunk driver in Yorkshire. At this point, the plumber never even considered the possibility of a link between the bad news and some jinx connected to the woman in black.

A fortnight went by without incident, and after attending the funeral of his young brother, Mr Jackson went on a five-hour bender round the clubs of Liverpool, accompanied by a beautiful waitress named Sara, whom he had been dating for over a month. That night was the first time the girl from Garston had stayed at the plumber's flat. They made love in Jackson's bed at around 10pm, and then decided to watch a few DVDs in the bedroom until they both started feeling tired at around 1.30am.

A little after three that morning, Jackson woke up to a slapping sound. Sara was sitting up slapping her right arm and shaking it about. 'Me circulation's gone ... it's all numb,' she winced. The plumber managed a weary 'Oh,' and within seconds was fast asleep again. Some time later, he was awakened by Sara kicking about violently in the bed, and he turned over with a groan to see what the matter was this time. One of the pillows was covering her face, and she was desperately trying to remove it, but it was clamped down on her so hard she was obviously suffocating. Jackson tried his best to prise the pillow off her but it wouldn't budge, and he could distinctly see the imprints of two rather petite hands in the pillow fabric.

'Stop it!' Jackson cried out, realising that the ghostly woman had returned. He pulled on the pillow with all his might, and suddenly, whatever was pressing it down decided to ease off, and Jackson fell backwards off the bed with the pillow still in his hand.

Sara sat up, gasping heavily, and by the moonlight streaming into the room through the window, saw Jackson get up with the pillow in his hand. 'You, you … stupid maniac!' she gasped, still breathless from her ordeal, 'You tried to kill me!'

'Sara, it wasn't me, I swear!' Jackson protested.

She was having none of it. She leapt out of bed and headed for the door, threatening to report her boyfriend to the police.

'Sara!' Mr Jackson shouted at the top of his voice, 'Listen up, love, it wasn't me, honest to god. You've got to believe me.'

'Then who the bloody hell was it then?' Sara yelled back, her hand on the door handle. 'I can't see anybody else in the room!'

Just then, the three remaining pillows on the bed rose up and threw themselves in turn, at Sara, who let out a terrified scream and ran into the living room. The plumber tried to calm her down but she told him she was going home, and she rang for a taxi to take her back to Garston.

Within a week, Mr Jackson had left the flat.

A few months later, he was replacing some pipes for a woman in Speke, and during a break from work the woman who had hired him, a Mrs Greaves, remarked how her daughter was having a 'terrible time' at a flat in Aigburth, because it was haunted. Jackson's ears immediately pricked up. Surely she couldn't be talking about the haunted house in Lark Lane? But by a sheer coincidence, she was. Mrs Greaves told the plumber how her twenty-two-year-old daughter Jade had seen a woman in black standing over her bed one morning at half-past three. Something had also dragged the duvet off and pulled her hair as she lay in bed. Jackson breathed a sigh of relief that he had got out of that infernal flat.

Tragically, I have since heard that Jade was involved in a motorcycle accident which left her with a damaged spine. She may never walk again.

I still receive accounts of the woman in black who haunts the Lark Lane flats, and she is apparently just as malevolent as ever. She also seems to have some artistic ability.

In 2009, Robyn, a young chemistry student, fell asleep whilst revising for an exam in the bedroom of her flat in the same haunted house, and when she awakened she caught a fleeting glimpse of a tall woman in a large bonnet and long, into-the-waist dress darting into the wall. When she had recovered from the shock of seeing the ghost in retreat, she switched on the light. Her notepad, upon which she had been scribbling revision notes, now had a curious doodle of a very basic face upon one blank page. Immediately below it there was an unintelligible scrawl, possibly of letters, and Robyn believes the doodle and illegible words were the work of the woman in black, for they were most definitely not on the page before she dozed off.

Thankfully, at the time of writing, Robyn has not been afflicted by the curse of the woman in black.

~

There are two female ghosts who are occasionally seen in Catharine Street in the city centre, and they come from very contrasting backgrounds. One is the spectre of a nurse who is often seen in and around Agnes Jones House, the former Women's Hospital Building on Catharine Street, which now accommodates students. Time after time I have received letters and emails from people who have seen the nurse, who has sandy-coloured hair, and sometimes carries a clipboard. She has been seen in the former hospital building in several flats, and on one occasion, in December 2008, the ghostly nurse was encountered at 10pm out on Falkner Street, where a motorist saw the apparition melt away as it crossed the road caught in the beams of his vehicle's headlamps. Those who have encountered the apparition have claimed that her appearance heralded some medical problem, but I cannot yet find evidence for these claims.

A much scarier female ghost who brings bad luck is said to haunt the other side of Catharine Street, and her presence is supposedly rooted in the reputation this street once had for being a red light district.

In 2003, a forty-nine-year-old Greek man named Giorgio went in search of a prostitute. Unknown to his wife, who was ill in bed recovering from food-poisoning,

Giorgio had driven from his home in the suburbs under the pretence of visiting a filling station to get cigarettes and paracetamol for a make-believe headache.

At close on four in the morning, the lustful Greek drove down to the city centre for a spot of kerb-crawling, and as he passed along Catharine Street, he saw a woman in her twenties standing about thirty yards from the red telephone call box (which is still there today) but at the last moment his nerves got the better of him and he drove on, accelerating left down Myrtle Street, towards the Philharmonic Hall. However, the attractive red-headed lady of the night, in her PVC coat, tight short skirt, fishnet stocking and stilettos, was imprinted on his brain, and so he made a sharp left turn into Sugnall Street, which was then a poorly-lit backstreet behind the Philharmonic Hall. Giorgio then drove slowly up Caledonia Street, emerging near the Caledonian pub on to Catharine Street again. There, as though tempting him, was the prostitute, still standing in the same spot, looking in his direction but not at him.

With heart palpitating and butterflies in his stomach, he slowed his down until he had come alongside the girl. He had fantasised about doing this many times, but had never had the courage to get this far before. He checked his rear view mirror, mindful of the late night police patrols. The road was deserted at this ungodly hour, and the unflattering pale orange luminance from the sodium street-lamps shone down on the road like a dead version of sunlight.

Scarcely believing he was actually doing it, Giorgio pulled up by the young woman, leaned over to wind down his passenger window, and unlocked the door. He wasn't sure what to say. Wasn't she supposed to ask him if he wanted any business? His mouth was dry and his heart was racing. His thoughts raced too. 'How much?' he asked, but the girl didn't reply. At close quarters the Greek businessman could see that the girl's face was extremely pallid, almost pale blue, and she was wearing a cream polo-neck top of some sort under her PVC jacket. Her eyes just seemed a featureless black, like a Goth who had gone overboard with the black panda eyeliner and mascara. Giorgio couldn't see the whites at all.

Without a word, the girl reached for the door handle and got in. There was no turning back for the Greek now.

'Put your belt on,' Giorgio advised her, because he knew the police could pull him over if they saw him carrying a passenger who hadn't belted up, and where might that lead?

The woman showed no reaction to his words. She simply sat there, seemingly in a world of her own. Giorgio tried to fasten the seat-belt round her, but her hand, which was icy cold, intercepted his perspiring hairy fist and roughly pushed it away.

Giorgio drove off, agitated, and slightly peeved at her unresponsiveness, and in his haste he crunched his gears. He had in mind a local secluded car park where he would commit the act, and wondered how much she would charge. With mounting nerves, he tried to make conversation throughout the journey, but the woman remained resolutely silent.

At around 4.20am, Giorgio brought his car to a halt in a car park on the Liverpool University campus, not far from Sydney Jones Library, and told the prostitute to get in the back seat. She obediently lay down as the Greek's dark eyes nervously scanned the nightscape beyond the car windows. There wasn't a soul about and there was a strange, almost deathly stillness hanging in the air that night. The unfaithful husband prepared himself for safe sex, and glanced backwards over the front seat, to survey the woman he would soon be having sex with. What he saw was to almost give him a heart attack. The redhead was lying down on the back seat, and where her head should have been, there was only the polo neck, dappled with dark glistening liquid. In her hands, which were lying just below her chest, was her own severed head, the cheeks of which were streaked with tears and mascara. The front of the PVC jacket was now streaked with rivulets of blood.

As Giorgio gawped, speechless, at the appalling spectacle, the beheaded woman's bloodied mouth opened and out of it came a stream of what sounded like gibberish. Giorgio stumbled out of the car, and as he raced across the car park, he made the painful mistake of trying to zip up his flies, but in his haste and confusion got his manhood caught in the zip. Still in agony, he staggered and fell into one of the bushes surrounding the car park, and somehow managed to ease the zipper free.

From the seclusion of the bushes he looked back at his car full of dread and confusion. What had happened to the woman? Had she been murdered? How was she able to talk if her head had been removed? So many questions which he couldn't begin to answer, and so he ran off, putting as much distance as he could between himself and the car, and all the time panicking about what he would tell his wife, and the police for that matter, when he reported his car stolen.

After a taxi-ride home, during which he tried to concoct a plausible story to explain his prolonged absence and the missing car, Giorgio told his wife he'd been carjacked by two men as he drove around looking for a filling station. The men had worn balaclavas and had pushed him out of the vehicle, leaving him stranded in the city centre. Giorgio claimed to have called the police, but in reality he had not been able to find the guts to do that, and the next day when he went to the car park he was greatly relieved to find his unlocked car still intact, and more importantly, minus the headless prostitute.

Needles to say, Giorgio never went kerb-crawling again after that night, but a few months later he was diagnosed with prostate cancer. After a few years of constant treatment, he was finally given the all-clear. To this day he somehow feels the cancer was some sort of payback for his attempted infidelity.

I have heard that the prostitute with the detachable head still has her patch in the city centre.

In 2006 I was a guest on a late-night radio phone-in and the topic was ghosts. A taxi driver asked me if I had ever heard of the ghost of a prostitute who haunts the Catharine Street area, and I said I had, but before I could even describe the apparition, the cabby said a friend of his had picked up this prostitute one evening, and had driven her to a lonely location close to the Anglican Cathedral. At this spot, in the shadows of the towering sandstone edifice, the red-haired woman had suddenly put her hands on either side of her face and wrenched her head off her shoulders. She had then held her disembodied head towards the shocked punter, who turned and ran off in shock.

The DJ hosting the radio phone-in thought the caller was joking and cut the cabby's conversation off in the middle of a sentence. I am not sure if the call was a wind-up. I have heard of many more accounts of the red-haired street-walker, but they may amount to little more than an urban legend.

A man who lived on Catharine Street from 1960 to 1994 told me that the prostitute's ghost is that of a twenty-seven-year-old woman named Anita, who had only been 'on the game' for a few months when she was tragically decapitated in a car crash, sometime in the late 1970s, or possibly early 1980s. The car she died in was being driven by Anita's pimp, and he survived, almost without a scratch.

The last report I had of the ghost was in November 2007. A security guard picked up a red-haired prostitute in a brownish PVC jacket. Her hair was tied back in a ponytail, and she wore stilettos and black fishnet stockings. On this occasion, as the guard drove along Smithdown Road towards his flat, he felt a rush of cold air in the vehicle, and so he turned to ask the prostitute if the passenger door was properly closed, but the passenger seat was empty, and only the faint sweet perfume of the ghostly prostitute remained.

DEADLY GHOUL OF THE EAST LANCS

In January 1981, a blizzard swept over the country, and the North West failed to escape the wintry onslaught. Twenty-four-year-old Daniel Burton, from Walton Lane, was seeing a girl in Clifton in Greater Manchester during that January, and one evening he had a row with her which ended with him storming out of her flat. He got on his motorbike while his girlfriend Debra came screaming after him in the thick snow. As she cried out for him to come back, she slipped and fell on her backside, and as Daniel sped off, she sat there, crying.

All of a sudden, Debra had a terrible feeling that a disaster was about to happen to her boyfriend; a grim premonition in her mind, in which she could actually see Daniel lying in the road with his arms and legs broken and jutting out at weird unnatural angles.

Daniel, meanwhile, embarked on his idiotic thirty-odd-mile journey back to Liverpool, where he intended to stay at his mum's house. He rode on through the falling snow, across black ice, towards the East Lancashire Road. Three times during the journey Daniel caught brief glimpses of the ghostly face of his girlfriend in front of him, floating in mid-air, and each time she was crying. Daniel put these visions down to the stress of driving in the treacherous conditions and the aftermath of the blazing row.

Then, all of a sudden, as he was travelling along near Haydock, Daniel saw a woman standing in the lay-by in the distance, trying to thumb a lift. He pulled up, and saw the hitch-hiker was a young woman in her early twenties, standing there, shivering in a long green dress. Her beautiful hair was long black and shiny, reaching halfway down her back, and it was flecked with snowflakes. She made a beautiful, if incongruous, picture on that freezing night. Daniel took off his helmet so he could hear what she was saying, and in a Liverpudlian accent, she said, 'Ah thanks, mate. Are you going to Liverpool?'

'Yeah,' Daniel said, 'I'm goin' to Walton Lane.'

'Oh, that's great,' said the woman, 'I'm goin' to Sparrow Hall.'

She was so eager to get on the bike she almost jumped on to the seat and threw her arms around Daniel's waist.

Daniel was rather taken aback by the girl's eagerness, and he self-consciously fidgeted with his helmet, feeling guilty somehow, because the only girl who had ridden on the bike up till then as his pillion passenger had been Debra. He asked the attractive hitch-hiker, 'If you don't mind me asking, what are you doing out in this weather at this hour, dressed like that?'

'Had a big argument with me fellah,' she told him, and she puckered her eyebrows and scrunched up her pretty little nose. Daniel could see now from closer quarters just how angelic-looking the hitch-hiker was. She had large dark eyes of either brown or green and the skin of her face was as perfect as porcelain.

Daniel started to put his helmet on, and said: 'Er, look, love, I haven't got a spare crash helmet, so let's hope we don't get pulled by the police.'

'Oh, stuff 'em!' she laughed, and Daniel kick-started the motorbike and moved off down the East Lancs Road. About ten minutes into the journey, he looked at the face of his passenger in his right-hand mirror. The girl's long glossy hair was billowing in the icy breeze, like some shampoo advert and her cherubic little face was snuggled into his shoulder. Her eyes were clenched shut against the glacial buffeting wind. And then all of a sudden. In his left-hand mirror, Daniel noticed a dark-coloured car, about 200 yards behind him. It seemed to be accelerating towards him, and so Daniel revved his 250cc engine and tried to put some distance between himself and the car, which was the only other vehicle on the road. The snow was getting visibly thicker as he sped down the road and he knew he was taking a risk speeding in those conditions.

The car following him picked up speed and flashed its headlights several times. Daniel increased his speed to eighty-five miles per hour – ludicrous in those conditions. He checked his right mirror once again – then did a double-take – the hitch-hiker's face was now a grinning skull, its now straggly long hair streaming from a bare scalp.

Shocked rigid, Daniel looked down at his waist, to find a pair of bony hands clinging on to him. Then those skeletal hands suddenly flew up and cupped themselves around Daniel's visor, so he couldn't see the road. Tearing along at nearly ninety miles per hour, the ghastly, bony fingers tapped at the helmet visor as they blocked his view, and Daniel tried desperately to remove them, but the ghoul persisted in obscuring his field of vision. Then one of the hands suddenly let go and started to yank at the motorbike's handlebars. Daniel tried to brake, but in one nightmarish moment, the bike spun out of control, then turned on its end, catapulting him into a ditch. Then everything went black.

When Daniel came to, he was lying on his back in the snow, and large flakes were drifting down on to his blood-spattered visor, seemingly in slow motion. A strange silence was all around, and a middle-aged man with tears in his eyes was kneeling close to Daniel, leaning over him. Daniel felt numb from his head to his toes, and couldn't even move his tongue to speak. He didn't feel ready to die, because he wanted to make up with his beloved Debra, and realised now that he had been a fool to ever leave her side, whether in snow or sunshine.

Daniel soon lost consciousness again, and woke up in Walton Hospital, where he eventually made a complete recovery from two broken legs, a shattered collar bone and torn rotator cuff, and severe concussion. No one gave any credence to the story about the hitch-hiking ghoul, believing it to be an hallucination brought on by the concussion.

However, a few years later, Daniel finally married Debra, and during the celebrations afterwards, he happened to overhear a guest sitting with a group of people in the corner mentioning the so-called East Lancs Hitch-hiker. This man claimed that, since the early 1960s, there had been several deaths on the East Lancs Road, caused by a woman in a green dress who appears on the lay-by near Haydock. This woman was said to deliberately sabotage the vehicles of any driver unwise enough to give her a lift. She had caused a scooter crash in the 1960s by jerking the handlebars violently, and had been known to do the same with the driving wheels of cars in which she was travelling.

Daniel felt vindicated by what he was hearing and also a sense of relief. He poured out his own experience to the wedding guest, including the mysterious car that had seemingly chased him on the night in question. The guest told him that there was nothing spooky about the person in the car; he was a man who had lost his son on that stretch of the East Lancs after the supernatural hitch-hiker had put the handbrake on, causing the car to overturn. His son had died instantly from a broken neck but his father had survived, and had become obsessed with laying the spiteful ghost to rest. The poor man had resorted to driving up and down the East Lancs at all hours of the morning. That's what the guest had heard, anyway.

I have researched the stories of the alleged ghoul of the East Lancs, and I have discovered similar reports of a being described as a 'hobgoblin', that used to jump out on to the horses drawing wagons and carriages on a dirt track, when turnpikes existed, where the East Lancs now runs. They say that the malevolent female ghoul still appears in the lay-by of the East Lancs, always around December and January, so drive carefully if you use that road during that period and maybe think twice before offering her a lift.

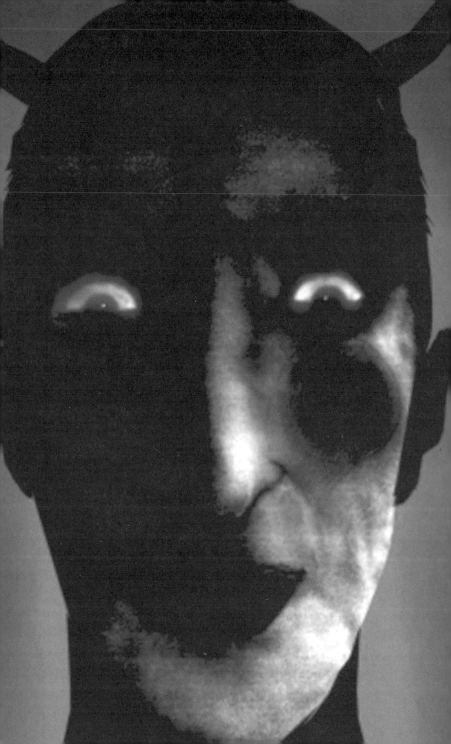

BOGEYMEN

THE RED FIEND OF BOLD STREET

Sometimes, when you are strolling down Bold Street, you may happen to notice a vacant shop, and if you do, you probably won't even give it a second glance, nor wonder why the premises happen to be empty. We are living in hard times, and there is nothing unusual about the closure of a shop on Bold Street, which is, in my humble opinion, Liverpool's finest and most atmospheric shopping thoroughfare, but the premises I am referring to really could be truthfully called the Little Shop of Horrors. Let me explain why.

In the 1970s, the shop did well for a while, because it was situated in a catchment area in close proximity to that much-missed emporium, the House of Holland. The shop in those days sold vacuum cleaners, televisions, five-band radios, washing machines and various other electrical household items. The owners had obtained the lease in the spring, and had found the shop quaint and welcoming, but as Christmas approached, strange incidents started happening. The lessee during this period was an Irishman by the name of Desmond, who bore a strong facial resemblance to the late Irish comedian Dave Allen.

One foggy afternoon in early December 1977, an old man came into the shop, inquiring about an electric razor, when he suddenly posed a curious question to Desmond, 'Has anything happened in here yet?' he asked.

'How d'you mean?' Desmond asked.

The old man said the building was haunted, and that even as a lad he'd heard strange tales about the place. 'Always in the run up to Christmas they say,' the pensioner remarked. 'That's why I asked.'

Desmond walked the eight feet into the stockroom to fetch the razor, but when he returned to the counter, the man had vanished – and yet the bell over the door hadn't sounded, and it was impossible to enter or leave the premises without that bell ringing. Then came the sound of an old man chuckling somewhere close by, but still he was nowhere to be found.

That night, Desmond went home to his flat on Huskisson Street and told his girlfriend Judy about the vanishing pensioner. She said she didn't believe in ghosts, it was all a load of rubbish and quickly changed the subject. She'd had what she called 'a bright idea'.

'Hey, listen to this, Des,' she said, barely containing her excitement. 'We're going to give up this flat and move in to the rooms over the shop!' and before Desmond could object, she added. 'No more rent money's going to be wasted on this dump. That way we can save up to get married!'

She presented it as a fait accompli, besides, Judy always mananged to get her own way somehow. And so, a week later, she and Desmond moved all their furniture into the rooms above the Bold Street shop. She decided they would leave their old bed at the flat, because there was a genuine Victorian double bed in the attic room of the Bold Street premises and they could use that.

On Christmas Eve, while Judy was at work, Desmond went up to the gloomy attic bedroom looking for his car keys. It was late afternoon and already getting dark. Light was shining under the attic door and Desmond was surprised to see silhouettes in the slit of light where someone's feet were pacing to and fro.

'Who's that?' he shouted nervously.

Suddenly, a substance that looked like blood began to ooze out from under the door, forming a vast spreading pool of scarlet. 'Jesus!' said Desmond, recoiling in horror, and rapidly retracing his steps back down the stairs. He rang Judy at work and told her what he'd seen, but she barely listened to a word he said. She was annoyed at him because she was due to attend her Christmas works party and he was holding her up. When she arrived at the shop later that night she greeted him with, 'Go on then, let's see what you were rattling on about.' She stormed up the stairs and found no blood and no signs of anybody. 'You're going round the bend,' was all she could say as she pushed past Desmond on the stairs.

'I am not going round the bend, and I am not sleeping in that attic tonight! I know exactly what I saw!' Desmond roared, and Judy told him that was fine, he could sleep on the shop counter then. He kept to his word, and spent an uncomfortable night on the shop floor that Christmas Eve. Meanwhile, up in the attic bedroom, Judy, still in a strop at what she took to be Desmond's wimpish behaviour, was about to have her own terrifying experience. She fell asleep at 1.15am, but sometime later was awakened by the violent rocking of the old bed. She felt it rise up, and the sensation of the ascent made her stomach turn over. It felt as if the bed had been lifted out of the attic and into the sky over Bold Street. Freezing winds buffeted the blankets, making them flap about, and Judy clung on to the mattress and cried out desperately for help.

She finally opened her eyes and to her amazement saw only the starry sky above her. The attic was gone. Then she turned to her right, and nearly jumped out of the bed. A malevolent-looking man with red-glowing skin was clutching the headboard with one hand and with the other was supporting the iron bed-frame under the palliasse. His pointed widow's peak hairline, evil penetrating eyes, turned up moustache and van dyke beard, perfectly framed the most hideous grin she had ever seen on a living face. She cringed with fear as the city lights sparkled far below and the dark glistening Mersey snaked to the left. She hoped she was dreaming, but knew she was not.

The bed suddenly tilted alarmingly, and Judy's tartan-clad hot water bottle rolled off the blankets and disappeared into the blackness.

'Say you'll be mine, Judy!' came the deep basso voice. 'Or you're going to follow that hot water bottle!' With a cackle of delight from the demonic creature, the bed tilted again at a crazy angle, and Judy slid screaming down to the bottom end, desperately grabbing at the bedding to save herself from certain death, but then, just as suddenly, it returned to a horizontal position. Judy was convinced that the red-skinned man was either the Devil himself, or one of his evil cohorts, and she suddenly remembered the rosary beads she kept under her pillow. She seized the rosary and thrust its silver crucifix at the would-be abductor, crying, 'Jesus Christ, please save me!'

The crimson creature let out a yowl, and let go of the bed to shield his eyes from the cross. The bed plummeted towards the ground. Judy, sick with apprehension, passed out. Whilst insensible, she had a vivid dream of glowing angel-like figures supporting the bed as they guided it back safely down to the attic. When she awoke, she got up and ran downstairs to tell Desmond what had happened. Desmond convinced her that the incident had been nothing more than a vivid nightmare, though, in truth, he had serious misgivings, but they both agreed that they would not be spending another day, never mind another night, at the shop.

Early the next morning, Christmas Day, while Desmond and Judy were on their way to the house of a relative with whom they hoped to stay, they passed St Luke's Church, and there, lying burst on the steps, was Judy's tartan-clad hot water bottle.

At the time of writing, the Little Shop of Horrors on Bold Street is currently empty. In the past I have had other reports of the enigmatic Red Fiend of Bold Street.

~

In 1985, two sisters, Kate and Megan, both in their thirties, decided to rent the premises, unaware, of course, of its reputation for being haunted. The sisters sold second-hand clothes from the shop, and Kate also made a bit of money selling her home-made jewellery.

In the summer of 1985, a heavily pregnant Megan was taken to the maternity hospital, leaving her younger sister Kate to run the shop on her own for five days. On the second day, Kate stayed late at the Bold Street shop, and decided to take a look at the dusty rooms upstairs. She finally reached the top of the house, after finding most of the other rooms empty, and was surprised to find an old king-sized bed up there, and beneath it, a battered-looking portmanteau full of vintage postcards from the Victorian and Edwardian era. There were also a number of books in the old case, including an 1881 copy of *Oates' Biographical Dictionary*, and, more curiously, a black leather-bound notebook of about 150 pages, half of which were filled with neat copperplate handwriting.

Fascinated by her find, Kate sat in the attic, poring over the faded brown writing. The subject of the notebook was 'The Djin' – an Arab term for demons and elemental beings. From the first page of the book Kate learned that the word 'genie' is derived from the Arabic word djin, and as she read on, she noticed that the handwriting became more and more erratic, and the word Shezzeral was underlined and written in capital letters within the text at several points. I have researched the many names of the demons of the djinn, and Shezzeral is not among them. What the word refers to is still a mystery to me.

As Kate struggled to decipher the wonky-looking longhand, utterly absorbed by the task, she suddenly heard a sound behind her – a creaking floorboard! Something – or someone – was now blocking out part of the daylight filtering into the attic via the skylight. Kate's heart missed a beat, and she turned to see what she could only describe as a shimmering column of what looked like green smoke, and at the top of the cylindrical vapourous mass, a terrifying face was gazing at her. The face was reddish orange, with piercing blue eyes, or possibly pale green. The face also had the tell-tale turned-up black moustache and van dyke beard.

Kate had difficulty getting to her feet, she was so afraid, and had to crawl on all fours to get to the door. She finally got to her feet and ran out of the attic as the walls began to reverberate with deep mocking laughter. She darted out of the shop without locking up and burst into a religious bookshop across the road, where she told a man what she had just seen. The man believed her story without hesitation. 'Stay there, love, I'll be back in a minute,' he said, sitting her down behind the counter, then bravely crossed the road into the shop and went up into the attic alone.

When he came out about five minutes later he told Kate the thing she had seen was a demon who had been invited into the attic 'a long time ago'. The man said he was a lay preacher, and offered to perform a 'cleansing ceremony' in the attic. Kate thanked him but declined his offer. When she told Megan what had happened, she admitted she too had heard strange sounds coming from the upper floors when she had been alone in the shop. She hadn't told Kate, not wishing to frighten her. The sisters decided to move.

~

In the 1990s, a man I shall call Ray, who ran a well-known shop in Bold Street, told me how, on several occasions, he and two other members of his staff had spotted an eerie reddish face peering out of the second floor windows of the vacant shop opposite. At first, Ray thought it was someone playing a prank, because the person peeping out of the window looked as if he was wearing a Halloween mask of the devil. A young member of Ray's staff, who had much keener vision than him, said it was no mask, but the man's actual face. What's more, the face seemed to float up the window, as if the person peeping out was levitating.

The identity of the Red Fiend is still unknown. The notebook Kate found in the haunted attic alluded to the Djin, and I can't help wondering if one of those diabolical spirits of Arabian legend had once been invoked in the attic of the haunted shop, perhaps during some arcane ritual. Such rituals, which open up portals to other realms, are known to the serious occultist.

Periodically, an unknown creature, resembling the mythological Pan, visits Liverpool. In January 1866, a great snow storm struck the city, and the gales and blizzards were so fierce, they blew down all the telegraph lines, so all communication between the city and the rest of the country was cut off for over a week. As temperatures plummeted below zero, the River Mersey froze over and Liverpool came to a complete standstill, as people remained indoors to escape the big freeze. Liverpool became a ghost town covered by an eiderdown of deep snow.

Then one morning, a policeman in Toxteth noticed strange tracks in the virgin snow: a trail of hoofprints, but aligned in a most peculiar manner. The animal that had made the prints had evidently placed one hoof exactly

119

eight inches in front of the other – in a precise straight line. The policeman, and anyone else for that matter, could think of no animal which could make such tracks. The constable and a colleague followed the curious trail across the snowbound city; up Renshaw Street and Lime Street, all the way to Scotland Road. At certain points the tracks had somehow climbed up high walls and across ivory-coated rooftops. At Scotland Road the tracks had come to a sudden halt – as if the eerie creature had vanished or flown off at that point.

Many of the superstitious Celts of Liverpool – the Irish, Welsh and Scots – believed there was something supernatural about the nature of the tracks. Who or what had hoofed feet and could walk up vertical walls? Spring-Heeled Jack, for all his abnormalities, had human feet, but what about 'the other fellah' – the Devil? In his Everton home, my great-grandfather, a Cornishman named George Slemen, told his Limerick wife about some similar tracks he had seen eleven years earlier in Devon. They too were believed to be the work of the Devil. George's account spread throughout the city and fed the fireside gossip and speculation that the Devil himself had walked amongst them.

The mystery deepened when many people claimed they had heard haunting pipe music early in the morning when the tracks were found. People's thoughts turned to Pan, the god of mischief, for he was always depicted in statues and illustrations as playing pipes, and he too had hoofed feet. Way back in the reign of King Richard I, a monk had written about a track of hoofprints that had appeared on the ground after a fierce lightning storm. They too remained unexplained.

In 1886, it would seem that the same creature made

several nocturnal visit to Liverpool – and this time it was observed by many witnesses, many of whom could not believe their eyes.

~

On 30 November 1886, the Liverpool Caledonian Association held its annual dinner to mark St Andrew's Day, at the Adelphi Hotel. Most of the dozens of guests were of Scottish birth or blood, and the great majority of them were military men. As you can imagine, the whiskey flowed freely that evening and the celebrations of all things Scottish went on into the wee small hours. A window was opened in the hotel suite to let out the cigar and tobacco smoke, and in its place a fog crept in.

Sir Donald Currie, a prominent MP, announced that some 'wild animal' was roaming about in the road in front of Lewis's department store, and everyone thought he was pulling their legs, but then a Major Hobart and a Captain Ching also spotted the same animal, just visible in the weak lamplight filtering through the fog. 'It's a damned ram!' Hobart declared, and soon windows were opening as the dinner guests looked out on to Renhsaw Street. 'Oh, it's just a prankster,' a doctor named Crawford said, seeing that the so-called 'ram' was now walking upright. Then they all heard the uncanny pipe music, and an army man named Blakely produced a revolver, took aim, and fired four shots at the unearthly entity. The creature fled off into the gloom, and the gunshots brought policemen hurrying to the Adelphi.

Just over a week later, on 7 December, 'Pan' returned again, and again was seen in what is now Ranelagh Place – situated between the Adelphi and Lewis's. On this

121

occasion, the Incorporated Law Society was honouring Liverpool's Lord Mayor John Hughes with a grand banquet, and over 150 distinguished guests, including prominent lords, MPs and even a member of the Rathbone family. Once again, the celebrations were protracted, and just after midnight, as heavy snow fell, several guests boarding carriages outside the Adelphi were startled when the horses started to whinny and become restless. The horned creature was seen again, and some accounts state that he was of a green cast, with two coiled horns set on a human-like head. The abomination's legs were covered in fur, with hooves where the feet should have been. The MP Sir Richard Cross was particularly affected by the appearance of the satyr-like entity after it approached his carriage at close quarters, and grinned menacingly at him. The exotic animals being kept at Lewis's Zoo that month were blamed for the Pan sightings, but none had escaped.

Then, later that month, on Christmas Eve, dozens of people saw the strange creature once again roaming Renshaw Street and Copperas Hill, and several policeman are even said to have made a concerted effort to corner and capture the being, but that morning, something catastrophic took place, which soon diverted the attention of everyone involved in the hunt.

At 1.40am, flames were spotted through the windows of Lewis's store and a fire of unknown origin soon took hold of the building. Tragically, many of the animals being kept at the store by the naturalist Mr Cross for a Christmas exhibition were roasted alive by the fire, including two bears. A polar bear and a Bengal tiger were rescued and hosed down later that morning, but Lewis's was reduced to a mound of smoking rubble, and with a massive clear-up operation to contend with, the authorities soon forgot about the strange sightings of 'Pan'.

The questions remain: Who or what was the weird figure? Was it some insane hoaxer, or was it truly something demonic? And could the supernatural visitant return to Liverpool one day?

THE HUYTON TOOTH-SNATCHER

One rainy night in April 2007, seventeen-year-old Amanda was startled from her sleep by strange sounds in the bedroom of her house on Huyton's Dinas Lane. The young Goth sat up and looked around the darkened room, which seemed even darker because Amanda had recently painted the walls black. She could see no one, but she had heard what sounded like muttering and had definitely heard a creak near the right side of her bed, made by someone standing on a loose bare floorboard there. Amanda winced with a slight pain in her left canine tooth. It had been throbbing all day, and she had tried to sleep off the toothache by going to bed earlier than normal, at 10pm.

Once the teenager was satisfied that there was no one lurking in her bedroom (which she called her 'Sanctum') she cocooned the duvet around her petite body and drifted off into the realms of dreams. Even in her dreams, Amanda was still aware of her toothache, and she dreamt she was deep in the heart of a forest, being pursued by a hunchbacked old woman all in black with grey hair tied up in a bun. The missahpen old woman wielded a pair of pincers, and Amanda knew that she intended to pull out her bad tooth. Amanda was naked, and when she ran off away from the old woman, she moved in slow motion. Every now and then, she would see grotesque faces peering out at her from behind trees in the wood, and at one point in the dream, one of these unearthly figures jumped out on Amanda and she awoke with a yelp, only to be confronted by something much more terrifying which has, so far, defied a rational explanation.

An old woman with a heavily lined face, hooked nose, dark-ringed eyes and a pointed chin, was leaning over Amanda's bed, with a pair of pincers in her hand gripping a blood-smeared tooth. Amanda experienced an agonising pain in her mouth. She ran the tip of her tongue round her gums and tasted salty blood – and discovered the hole in her swollen gum where the left canine had been wrenched out. The old woman let out a hissing chuckle, which enraged Amanda, who was already upset and distressed by the pain in her mouth, and she slapped the old hag hard across the face. The elderly stranger let out a yelp of surprise, and looked in astonishment at the teenager.

'Mum!' Amanda screamed as she got out of bed, 'Dad!' and she began throwing objects at the sinister tooth-snatcher. An old-fashioned alarm clock was the first missile to be aimed at the wizened intruder, who screamed as it bounced off her head, then ran into the corner of the black-walled room, to a gap between the wall and the wardrobe, and at that moment the bedroom door burst open and Amanda's father came in and switched on the light. Amanda ran to him and flung her arms round his waist for protection – something she hadn't done for a very long time – and told him what had just happened and urged him to look in the niche between the wall and wardrobe, which he did, somewhat gingerly, but found nobody there. 'You obviously had a nightmare, Mandy.' But Amanda was adamant that she hadn't – and she opened her mouth wide and showed her father the missing tooth, which could not possibly have come out on its own.

Amanda's mother entered the bedroom and when she heard the eerie story, suggested that Amanda had perhaps pulled her aching tooth out in her sleep. Amanda was furious at the suggestion. 'Course I didn't!' she protested, 'How could I? It was a massive molar, for god's sake!' and she pointed out the bloodstains on the duvet. Amanda's father searched everywhere, but there was no sign of the tooth. It was never found, and a few week later, Amanda had a false canine implanted in her gum by the dentist.

What Amanda and her parents did not know, was that there had been similar tooth-snatching incidents in Huyton stretching back to the 1930s at least, and in 1978, in Lincombe Road – the neighbouring road to Dinas Road – there were two strange cases of nocturnal tooth-theft.

In March 1978, a woman awoke one night to find a white-haired old woman in a long black robe, leaning over the bed of her four-year-old daughter who was crying. When the mother shouted out at the figure, it immediately vanished. When the light was switched on, the little girl was sobbing and clutching her mouth. Her front teeth had gone. Centuries ago, some witches stole the milk-teeth of infants to use in spells.

In September of that same year, in the same road, the visiting grandfather of a family had had a bit too much to drink at his grandson's twenty-first birthday party, and retired to the guest bedroom at almost three in the morning to sleep it off. The old man, Jeffrey, only had a single tooth left in his head, and was often mocked because of it. His late wife had repeatedly tried to persuade him to have the tooth pulled out and to get a proper set of dentures, but he was terrified of the dentist, and needles in particular.

Jeffrey was so drunk, he fell asleep on the bed without even undressing and settled into a welcoming sleep, but around half-past three he awoke with the sensation of an icy hand on his chest and cold bony fingers probing his mouth, yanking at his single tooth. As he squinted into the darkness, he saw a white-haired woman, engrossed in pulling at his tooth. Jeffrey tried to get up, but the old woman seemed to have superhuman strength, and she pinned him down on the bed with her left hand as her right hand grappled with the solitary tooth. He tried to scream but his call for help was muffled by the old woman's fingers in his mouth. Then he felt a sharp agonising pain as his tooth was twisted and wrenched from his jawbone. As the tooth was giving way, the old woman jumped up and down on him, squealing and grinning to reveal that she herself had only one tooth.

Unable to move, Jeffrey retaliated in the only way he could by spitting in his assailant's face, and noticed that his spittle was tinged with blood. At last, Jeffrey somehow summoned enough strength to push the entity off him, and he heard her land heavily on the floor at the side of the bed and let out an ear-piercing scream. Moments later, the door flew open, and Jeffrey's son and nephew came into the room. The light was switched on, and Jeffrey was stumbling away from the bed with blood streaming from his mouth. He gave a garbled account of the old woman who had pulled his tooth out, but his son could see that the tooth in question was still there, although it was very loose and looked ready to fall out. Jeffrey gargled with mouthwash, took an aspirin, and then swigged two glasses of neat whiskey to deaden the pain from his dislodged tooth. He laughed about the 'strange nightmare' – for that's what his son convinced him the incident really was, and within the hour, Jeffrey was once again in the guest bedroom, sinking into sleep, topped up with fine whiskey and aspirin. At a quarter-past five that morning, the old hag returned. Jeffrey felt the alarmingly familiar icy hand on his chest, steadying him as the bony cold finger and thumb of the other hand seized the grandfather's loose tooth – and this time, wrenched it out in one go.

Jeffrey cried out in pain. The aspirin and whiskey had only fractionally dulled the agony of such a brutal extraction. The creepy old woman was surprisingly sprightly for her advanced age, and like a flash, had flitted into the darkness of the room, though Jeffrey could hear her sniggering close by. He over-strained his vocal cords, leaving him unable to cry out again.

Moments later, the door flew open, and in came Jeffrey's eighteen-year-old grand-daughter Kerry. She switched on the light, and hurried over to her distressed grand-dad, who was unsteadily trying to get up off the bed with his hand to his mouth. He tried to tell Kerry what had happened, but she too was trembling, and started pulling Jeffrey towards the door with so much force, he almost fell over. Kerry was met by other members of the family as she reached the doorway. Slamming the door behind her she told them all, 'She's still in there! I saw her!'

Kerry's father gave her a quizzical look and went to open the door, but Kerry blocked his way saying, 'No, don't, Dad! She's horrible! I mean it.'

Kerry's father (who was Jeffrey's son) opened the door anyway, and made a search of the room. He could find no old intruder, but there was a sickly sweet smell in the air that lingered in that room for days. Kerry said that as she had entered the room that morning after hearing her grandfather cry out, she had seen a scary-looking old woman of about only five-feet in height, in a long black robe, hiding between the wardrobe and a bookcase. Kerry had pretended not to see the old woman at first, but as she had helped her grandfather out of the room and glanced back, the old woman realised she had been spotted and screwed up her face in such a grotesque way, that it was imprinted on her mind for years afterwards.

As in other cases of this sort that I have researched, the grandfather's tooth was never found. Incidentally, Old Hag Syndrome incidents are currently on the increase across the North West. Sleep well tonight ...

RED EYES

Around 10.20pm, on a windy October night in 1977, thirty-nine-year-old Jean left an amusement arcade on London Road where she worked as a cashier, and decided to walk home to her house on Marmaduke Street. As she walked along West Derby Street, Jean experienced the unsettling sensation of being watched – as if hidden eyes were upon her. For some reason she felt the eerie watcher was standing across the road in the shadows of the silhouetted Harrison Jones School, so she increased her pace as the knife-edged autumn wind sent shrivelled-up leaves spiralling about her. The road was unusually quiet that night and at the best of times Jean hated walking through this secluded corner of the Paddington district.

All of a sudden, two points of fiery red light appeared in front of the cashier, and immediately, she stopped dead. The lights looked like two glowing eyes and hung in the air, about five feet or more from the ground – almond shaped and of a luminous crimson, with flame-yellow irises. Jean shivered with nerves, and bolted across the road with her heart pounding, afraid to look back in case the menacing red eyes were following her.

Jean was massively relieved when she spotted a former neighbour, fifty-year-old Mrs Mary Armstrong, on the other side of the road, walking past Paddington Comprehensive on her way to her daughter's house on Smithdown Lane. Jean rushed across and told Mary what had just happened. Mrs Armstrong astonished her friend with her sombre reply, 'I've seen them, Jean.' she went on to explain that she and her daughters had seen the red eyes in the previous October, just before Duck-Apple Night (as Halloween was then called) by St Mary's Church, just up the road on Irvine Street. 'We watched them darting round in the church cemetery,' Mary told her frightened friend, adding, 'you ask our Patricia and Bernadette.'

'Well there's no way I'm going home that way now,' Jean said, and she linked arms with Mary and went the long way home via Smithdown Lane.

For many years that creepy pair of red eyes haunted the Edge Hill, Paddington, Kensington and Wavertree districts of Liverpool, and encounters always peaked in the nights of late October, leading up to Halloween.

In the mid-eighties, the reports ended as mysteriously as they had begun, but now, it would seem that old Red Eyes is back once again, and this time the setting is Huyton.

At 10.45pm on the Saturday night of 2 October 2010, twenty-seven-year-old Kayleigh was watching television to while away the lonely hours while her husband Mike worked nights as a security guard. Kayleigh's three-year-old daughter Connie began to scream up in her bedroom, and within seconds her mum was bounding up the stairs, because her child did not usually sound so distressed. As Kayleigh entered the bedroom, she saw two red points of light shining through the lace curtains from outside, and for a moment she assumed some idiot with a laser pen was messing about, but when she lifted the curtains, she was confronted with a terrifying, inexplicable sight. A pair of luminous scarlet eyes hung in the air, just inches away outside the window, looking directly in at Kayleigh. She recoiled in shock and went to grab Connie, then rushed downstairs with the child and put her down in an armchair. After bolting the front door, Kayleigh rang her mother to tell her what she had seen. Kayeigh's mum argued that the so-called 'eyes' must have been a reflection of a car's brake lights, but Kayleigh retorted that the eyes had been only too real, glowing and hideous-looking.

Minutes later, out of curiosity, Kayleigh went back to her daughter's room and again looked out of the window. Within seconds the demonic red eyes came floating out of the night air towards the window. Kayleigh immediately ran out of the room and this time rang her husband, begging him to come home.

The next day, before Kayleigh had even mentioned the weird incidents to anyone outside her home, her neighbour came over to tell her about about 'strange red lights' that she had seen hovering about at her bathroom window at three in the morning.

Since then I have received two more recent reports from residents in Huyton who have seen the spooky red

132

eyes floating down Longview Drive, close to St Thomas Becket High School, around midnight. These sightings took place on Tuesday 19 October 2010. If you are out when October comes around, keep your eyes peeled for old Red Eyes; he may even see you first ...

When researching supernatural incidents that have been reported to me, it's often difficult to establish the exact date on which they took place, no matter whether it was last week, or decades ago. Some people are blessed with a perfect, almost photographic memory, and can easily recall what they had for tea on a certain date three years ago, whereas other people can't even agree on what day they tied the knot, without consulting their marriage lines. I couldn't tell you what I had for lunch yesterday, and yet I can remember entire conversations I've had from several years ago. Memory is a very fickle and unreliable thing, as any detective or policeman taking down statements of a reported crime from witnesses will tell you. Their testimony rarely agrees on even the major points; the getaway car was red, one will say, and another witness will swear blind it was white, and so on.

In the following case, the witness, Sharon, was only thirteen, yet she remembers the night she first encountered a weird entity because of two things: her grandfather had treated her to ice cream and strawberries as he sat watching a televised cricket match between England and Australia, and later on that summer's day, she and her grandfather had laughed together as they watched that legendary episode featuring the comic genius Tony Hancock, in which he decides to become a blood donor. These two recollections – the cricket match and the blood donor episode – would mark the memorable date as Friday, 23 June 1961.

On that Friday evening, at nine o'clock, Sharon heard a rapping sound in the upstairs bedroom of her house on Balliol Road, Bootle, and went up to investigate. She had a good look round but could find nothing to account for the rapping, and just as she was about to leave the room, she heard another three loud taps which seemed to come from the headboard of her old bed. This spooked her and she hurried downstairs to fetch her mother. However, Sharon's mum was too preoccupied making salmon spread sandwiches to take outside for a group of neighbours, who were sitting out on their front doorsteps on this warm evening, smoking, drinking orange juice, and enjoying a good old gossip.

At around half-past eleven that same night, Sharon went to bed, and, feeling a bit uneasy as she recalled the strange sounds she'd heard earlier, she decided to read the glossy magazine her mother bought each month called *Emergency Ward 10*, based, of course, on the popular television series of the same name. The magazine was basically a glorified comic strip, with stills from the series, and it featured the usual diet of hospital drama and romance between the doctors, nurses, and sometimes even the patients.

Well, Sharon had recently started to fancy the idea of becoming a nurse herself, and as she read the magazine on this humid June night, she started to doze off, and in-between waking and falling asleep, strange images came into her mind. Fragments of the Tony Hancock blood donor sketch were mixed up with scenes from the magazine, and throughout the surreal semi-conscious ramblings of her dream, she could even smell the sharp antiseptic odour that often hangs in the air in hospitals.

In the midst of Sharon's kaleidoscopic jumble of a dream, she suddenly felt an excruciating pain in her left big toe, and winced with the pain. As she woke up fully, something backed away from the bottom of her bed. Sharon heard it shuffle, and bleary eyed, she squinted into the shadows, asking, 'Mum, is that you?'

The teenager's feet had been sticking out from under the thin candy-striped sheet, seeking the relative coolness of the smooth wooden board at the bottom of the bed, and Sharon could see a red spot on her left toe where it throbbed. She examined it and saw it was a puncture mark, and, what's more, there was another, similar one on the other side of the same toe. Stranger still, the antiseptic odour that Sharon had smelt in her dream now filled the bedroom.

Sharon believed she had been bitten by nothing more sinister than some summer insect, and she turned over, and tried to go back to sleep, but then came the same rapping sounds she had heard earlier that day. A floorboard beneath the linoleum creaked. Someone was definitely sneaking about by the bottom of the bed. Sharon slowly turned around, and propping herself up on one elbow, saw the oddest sight. A bizarre little old man was standing at the foot of the bed in a pair of blue-striped pyjamas. He was no more than about three-and-a-half feet in height, and his left hand rested casually on the board at the bottom of the bed. Protruding from the right rolled up sleeve of his pyjamas was a thin wrist with only a deformed-looking thumb and index finger resembling pincers, attached to it. The pointed nails of this pincer hand tapped on the bed's board, whilst the stranger's large globular head was bandaged, with a blood stain seeping through the bandage over the forehead. The peculiar little personage also had a long pointed nose and a pair of incredibly dangerous-looking eyes that were fixed on Sharon's own. The man suddenly puckered his lips, causing a steady stream of blood to spurt out and splatter on to the lino.

Sharon screamed, and the flow of blood from the night visitor's mouth instantly ceased. He grinned, revealing a few yellow teeth, and an almost reptilian tongue which he poked out at Sharon in a mocking gesture. 'Oh, do be quiet,' he rasped, and his pincer hand suddenly lunged at Sharon's big toe again and the hard nail-like substance of the grotesque thumb and forefinger clicked together, sending a shooting pain up her leg. Sharon quickly withdrew her feet under the blanket and screamed again, and then something even more unaccountable took place. Sharon's father, who was a thickset, broad-shouldered docker, and her grandfather, burst through the bedroom door in response to the girl's screams, and a split-second before they came into the room, the freakish-looking toe-pincher seemed to collapse into the floor in one impossibly swift movement.

Sharon's tale would not have been given any credence, only for the pool of red liquid on the floor near the foot of her bed. The fluid smelt vile, but within minutes it seemed to evaporate, and in the morning no trace could be found of the blood. The strong antiseptic smell, however, hung in the air for days.

Sharon slept in the same room as her parents for three days, until she was able to gather the courage to sleep in her own bedroom again. The girl's mother thought she had merely suffered a nightmare, and would jokingly ask Sharon if she had seen 'Mr Pinches' lately, and more often than not, Sharon would respond by storming out of the room and into the backyard for a sulk, and who could blame her? The girl had had a terrifying encounter with something neither she, nor any adult, could explain.

After his initial appearance, Mr Pinches made himself scarce for several months, but in September of that year, he returned unexpectedly one morning just after 3am. Sharon was coming back from the toilet, half asleep, when her bare foot slid on something wet on the floor, just inside her bedroom. She couldn't see what the puddle was at first, but as her eyes adjusted to the darkened bedroom, the liquid looked reddish – and at the same time her nostrils detected that horrible antiseptic smell again, which she automatically associated with Mr Pinches.

Sharon's stomach turned over as she realised her 'bogeyman' was back, and she turned, intending to run out of the room, but there he was, the misshapen dwarf with the bandaged head and the deformed hand, leaning against the now shut bedroom door, blocking her escape route. Sharon could see his lower half this time. He wore blue-striped trousers that matched his pyjama top, but his bare feet had weird long splayed-out toes. The dwarf-man lunged at Sharon, who turned and ran to the side of her bed screaming loud enough to wake the dead. She ran across the bed and round the back of him to the door. She recalls yanking the door open to escape, and the sound of the pulled-back door hitting the creepy little man's head with a thud. She bumped into her father, who was already halfway across the stair-landing after hearing her screams, but Sharon was still so terrified of Mr Pinches getting her, she struggled from her father's grip and ran into his room, where her mother was sitting up, half asleep.

Sharon's father searched her bedroom, but could find no trace of the alleged entity beyond the watery-red stain on the lino, although that dreadful antiseptic odour hung in the air again. After that night, the thing never returned, and a year later, the family moved out of that house on Balliol Road to a house in Norris Green.

I mentioned this story on a BBC radio programme, and not long afterwards, several people wrote to me with some intriguing reports of very similar experiences.

~

A man named Geoff wrote to tell me how, in 1965, he had been a twelve-year-old lad living on Hawthorne Road, just a stone's throw from Balliol Road where Sharon had lived in Bootle. On the first day of the school holidays – which would have been Saturday, 17 July 1965 – Geoff woke up with strange dark spots all over his feet. When he looked closely at the spots, he could see they were puncture marks with bruising around them. Geoff showed the bruises to his mum, and she thought they might be flea-bites, even though the family didn't have any cats or dogs.

Then, about a week later, Geoff awoke at around 1.20am one morning, and felt a sharp stabbing pain in his left foot. Looking down towards the end of the bed, he saw something incredibly agile dive to the floor, then scuttle under the bed. Geoff only got a fleeting glimpse of the thing, but thought that it looked 'whitish'. When the boy turned the light on, he dared to look under the bed and saw nothing there except an old tennis ball and some bits of fluff. Geoff examined his throbbing foot and found a tiny hole in the sole that was still bleeding. The thing that had apparently inflicted the wound was never seen again.

~

Jane Adams, who lived in the Breeze Hill area of Bootle, in very close proximity to the houses where Geoff and Sharon had lived, wrote telling me how, in 1970, when she was six years of age, something used to pinch her all over as she lay in bed. She would wake up covered in bruises, and sometimes, when she awoke during the night in the middle of one of the 'pincher's' sadistic attacks, she would find herself unable to move a muscle, but, terrifyingly, she could hear something chuckling just outside her fixed field of vision. The attacks occurred on an almost nightly basis for about three months.

Jane's mother once had to sleep in her daughter's bedroom, to make room for guests staying at the house and Jane went to stay with her grandmother in West Derby for a few days. When she returned home, she saw that her mother's legs and arms were covered with the same type of tiny bruises and minute puncture marks that she had suffered for the last three months. Both mother and daughter noticed a smell reminiscent of the antiseptic cream Germolene when they awoke in the room in question in the morning, very similar to the disinfectant smell that Sharon and members of her family had detected during the attacks by 'Mr Pinches' in 1961.

The identity of Mr Pinches has not been determined. I had hoped to find evidence of someone matching his physical description in the Bootle area; someone who had perhaps been hospitalised at some point, but so far, my search of censuses and medical records has not thrown up any leads, but I'll keep looking into this strange case.

THE OLD MAN IN THE CARPET

The following baffling story unfolded in the autumn of 2002, when a couple from Anfield, Kevin and Jenny, bought what they regarded as their dream house in north Liverpool. As soon as the estate agent had shown them round the five-bedroom Victorian house and garden,

Kevin and Jenny instantly fell in love with it. The couple's two young children, Alfie and Kelly, also instantly loved the house, and when all the paperwork had been finalised and the family moved in, the children enjoyed playing in the garden, which has a very quiet and almost sleepy atmosphere about it.

Shortly after their move, an elderly neighbour walking his dog stopped to chat to the couple, and said something that made them feel a bit uneasy. 'It's a lovely place by day,' he said, 'but ... I don't know ... it just seems to change its character at night.'

Rather annoyed by this old man's unsolicited opinion of their lovely house, Jenny asked him exactly what he meant by it. The old man quickly realised that he'd said something he shouldn't have and, back-pedalling, came back with a rather lame reply: 'Oh, nah, it's just my imagination, love. A lot of places have a different feel of a night don't they? That's all I meant, like. Take no notice of me.'

That evening, an October chill descended on the house – just the excuse the family had been waiting for to light a real fire. Kevin proudly put coal in the grate of the cast-iron fireplace in the living room as his children watched. He loved open fires, and the children helped him twist bits of newspaper into tapers which they inserted between the nuggets of coal. In no time a roaring fire was kindled and the family gathered around the rosy flames that autumn night and couldn't think of anywhere they would rather be. Kevin told the children stories, and said that the little blue flames that popped up in the fire now and then were really fairies, dancing. Kelly, who was only five, loved her dad's stories, and seven-year-old Alfie gleefully reminded him that Halloween was only a few weeks away. Kevin imagined the atmospheric ghost stories he could tell on Duck-Apple Night in front of the quaint open fire and smiled as he patted Alfie's head.

At about half-past eight that evening, Jenny took Kelly up to the bathroom and supervised her as she brushed her teeth before bedtime. As Kelly rinsed her mouth over the wash basin, she and her mum were startled by excited cries coming from downstairs. Those cries came from Alfie, who ran upstairs to his father, who was painting a spare room, crying, 'Dad! There's a face in the fire! Come and look!'

'Hang on, Alfie. Let me just wipe this paint off my hands,' said the boy's father, trying to suppress his impatience. He had only just got started on the room, but being the good father he was, he reluctantly left it to follow Alfie downstairs, and they both bumped into Jenny and little Kelly on the landing.

'Mum, there's a boy's face in the fire!' cried Alfie.

'Okay, we all heard you the first time, Alfie. We're coming now.'

And so the whole family trooped downstairs and into the living room. As they reached the living room doorway, Jenny said to her husband, 'You'll have to stop telling them stories, Kev,' and they both laughed. But they all stared in disbelief when they came into the living room and looked at the fire. As clear as in a photograph, was the image of a boy of about ten, in the glowing embers, and he looked as if he was crying.

'Jesus!' Jenny gasped, grabbing Kevin's arm, 'Oh Kevin, what on earth is it?'

Kevin made it a point never to swear in front of his children, but on this occasion he couldn't help himself. He then spoke sharply to his son, 'Come back here, Alfie!'

because Alfie was walking towards the realistic apparition, as if mesmerised by the flickering spectre.

The apparition of the child shimmered but was clear for them all to see, and it then began wringing its hands, as if pleading for something, help perhaps. Then a faint high-pitched scream could be heard, and suddenly, the image was obliterated by the flames. At that precise moment, the plasma television in the corner, which had been muted earlier, let out a deafening blast of sound, as if something mischievous had pressed the mute-off button on the remote-control.

That evening, Alfie and Kelly were allowed to sleep with their mum and dad because they had been so upset by the appearance of the boy in the fire, but that was only mild compared to what was about to follow. Oh yes! Things were going to get much worse.

A few days later, Kelly suddenly announced at breakfast that a 'naughty old man' had sat on her bed the night before and slapped her arm and leg. She said she had watched him come out of the carpet, and when she had started crying he had called her a 'little scut'. The child had obviously never heard this word before, and for that matter, neither had Kevin. He did a little research and discovered it was an old Victorian swear-word. A scut is the tail of a hare, but was also used derogatorily as an uncomplimentary archaic four-letter word. Kelly was asked to sketch the man from the carpet, and drew him as tall and skinny and bald, with tufts of long grey straggly hair on each side of his head. He had warned her that if she told anyone where he came from, he'd come for her in the middle of the night and take her back into the carpet with him. 'He said I'd never see my mummy and daddy again,' Kelly whimpered, as she buried her face in her mother's neck. 'I don't want him to get me, Mum. Please don't let him get me.'

Kevin didn't know what to make of this story. It was he who had found the old carpet in the attic, and Jenny had suggested getting it cleaned professionally because it had a beautiful pattern on it. It had then been laid out in Kelly's bedroom and she had been very pleased with it. Alfie added to the mystery by saying that he had heard a stranger talking to Kelly in her room on the night of the alleged ghostly visitation, but his parents weren't sure if the whole thing was all just down to Kelly having a nightmare and her brother adding fanciful bits to it, as children do.

However, the carpet had to be removed from Kelly's room, because the mere sight of it continued to upset her, and it was then laid down in her parent's bedroom by Kevin. The move had taken their every last penny and they were not about to discard a perfectly good carpet.

Weeks went by without incident, but then one morning at around 3am, Jenny awoke, and turned over because Kevin was snoring in her face. Moonlight was pouring through the window on to the bedroom floor, on to the old carpet. Jenny idly gazed at the pattern through half closed eyes, about to go back to sleep, when she saw lumps rise up in it. At first, she thought mice must be scampering about under it, because the lumps moved slightly, but soon a face began to form in the carpet, and she froze with expectation. In one swift movement, an ash-grey figure of a bald-headed man appeared on the carpet, with hair at the sides of that head and a long hooked nose. In the moonlight, Jenny could see every detail of the ghost: his waistcoat and the chain of his fob watch, his long coat, narrow trousers and boots.

146

By now, Jenny's hand was moving stealthily under the covers towards her husband's arm, and she shook him and even pinched him as he snored loudly. Meanwhile, the ghost lifted itself up off the carpet, and chillingly bent over to look at Jenny with his head tilted. Jenny closed her eyes tight, as the little man's shallow breathing could be felt close to her left ear. Then she heard footsteps padding across the room. All attempts at subterfuge were now gone, and Jenny shook Kevin with so much violence she knocked his head against the headboard. 'Ouch! What are you playing at, Jen? That wasn't funny.'

She told him what had just happened, but Kevin only turned his head into the pillow and mumbled, 'It's been a dream,' and then he turned over, ready to go back to sleep.

The next moment loud screams could be heard coming from Alfie's room. Jenny flew from her bed and rushed into her son's room. Alfie was hidden under the blankets, wailing. Jenny pulled the blankets away, 'Are you alright, sweetie? What's the matter?'

'He tried to strangle me, Mum!' Alfie pointed at something Jenny could see out the corner of her right eye. A tall figure was half hidden on the other side of the wardrobe to her right, but she was too scared to turn her head to face the weird ghost. Jenny picked up her son as he screamed hysterically, and carried him out of the room to her own bedroom. She called her husband every name under the sun because he had ignored her cries for help.

On the following morning, Jenny had a strange impulse to hang the accursed carpet on the washing-line in the garden, and she beat it repeatedly with a cricket bat. Dust came off it, and she and Kevin heard weird faint screams which seemed to actually come from inside the fabric of the carpet. Jenny couldn't take any more. There and then she doused the carpet in fire-lighter fluid and burnt it in the back garden and threw away the ash. She didn't want a single trace left in her house of the accursed rug. Thankfully, since then, there have been no further paranormal incidents at the house.

Spirits, particularly evil ones, are said to be able to hide and take refuge in certain objects and places, supposedly to hide from demons that call to collect them and take them to Hell. I'm not sure if I can accept that explanation, though it is possible that the essence of a person's spirit may become attached to an inanimate object which meant a lot to that person after death.

In Edwardian times, for example, there was a case reported in which a dark vapourous entity was often seen to come out of a gold locket in a manner we would usually associate with the archetypal genie. The locket, which contained a carefully spiralled lock of Titian-red hair, was found by a broker in the attic of his house on Wagstaff Street, Toxteth Park, in 1907. A maid who entered the broker's chamber to make his bed after her master had departed for work, watched the nebulous ghost slowly materialise as a steady outpouring of black vapour from the locket, which lay opened on a bedside cabinet. The servant girl screamed and ran out of the room to fetch a butler, who also witnessed the cloudy humanoid figure floating about the room.

The aeriform apparition was reported to the master of the house, and days later, he himself witnessed the dramatic materialisation, and made the mistake of standing his ground and attempting to communicate with the nebulous spirit. The entity is said to have responded to the broker's question: 'Who are you?' with an attempt to throttle him with a pair of black hands that seemed to solidify in mid-air. The broker and his servants fled the house, and after the ghost had made itself scarce, the locket was either thrown or given away, and nothing more is known about this intriguing haunting.

The homicidal smoky spectre had obviously sought refuge within the locket of red hair for some long-forgotten reason; perhaps the hair belonged to a lover of long ago, or could the hair have been clipped from the head of a murderer after he had been hanged at the gallows? Such morbid talismans were common once.

THE THING IN ABERCROMBY PARK

The other day I was walking through the Georgian splendour of Abercromby Square when I recalled the old dark legend about the so-called 'Hanging Tree', which stands in Abercromby Park, close to the Oxford Street entrance, which, in turn, lies adjacent to the old Senate House building. Living on Myrtle Street in my youth, I was well-acquainted with the legends and folklore of the neighbourhood, and tales about the Hanging Tree of Abercromby Park would crop up every now and then. Several tramps allegedly hanged themselves from the tree in question, over a period of time in the late 1960s, and a number of accidental deaths have taken place under it.

I recall hearing about a heroin addict who overdosed in the park, and his body was found at the base of the tree. Then there was a student, supposedly in the best of health, who, with time on her hands between lectures, fell asleep under the accursed tree one glorious summer afternoon. She never woke up. She had died from that rather vague-sounding phenomenon known as 'natural causes' whilst asleep.

Not long afterwards, a vagrant who was a well-known character in the area (who I can clearly recall begging for money on Brownlow Hill, near to the Parry Books bookstore) was also found dead under the same tree with his eyes wide open and a look of sheer horror on his face. Beside him lay a half-bottle of rum. He had died from exposure, even though he was found on a mild August afternoon.

Abercromby Square plays host to many more ghosts, both old and modern, each with histories that have been unravelled, but I cannot for the life of me unravel the story behind the Hanging Tree. However, here is a strange but curious piece of information which might throw some light on the unearthly conundrum.

A policeman named Stan, who had a beat on Abercromby Square in the 1950s, once told me how, one wintry moonlit morning in 1951, at around 4am, he was walking up Oxford Street, from the direction of the Oxford public house, when he crossed the road and halted for a moment to look into the park, because he thought he saw something in the moonlight darting across the lawns. The dark object moved so rapidly, it was almost too fast for Stan's eyes to follow. The policeman's curiosity was sufficiently aroused for him to linger a while, observing the park from the shadows of St Catherine's Church (which was later demolished to make way for Senate House) for a few minutes longer, until his eyes had adjusted to the dark.

And then Stan saw the thing, and this inadequate and indeterminate word is the only one the policeman could ascribe to the dark amorphous object he watched, crawling about on that very same tree that has such grim associations with so many deaths, which have unnaturally occurred under its spreading gnarled boughs. Police personnel are, first and foremost, trained observers, and Stan told me in precise detail what he observed that night: One moment the thing appeared sausage-shaped, and it was camouflaged to blend into the same colours and shades that surrounded it. It would stretch to about five feet long one moment, and then it would contract and seemingly flatten, until it had reformed into a two-dimensional black disc.

It moved with an unusual undulating, quivery type of motion, and when the policeman gave a little cough, it stopped dead, as if it hadn't been aware it was being watched until that moment. He waited for about a minute, and then saw it darken the base of the large tree near the gate. 'It slithered up the tree and I lost sight of it in the shadows. It really unnerved me, because I didn't know what the thing was, and still don't, for that matter. I was glad when I was back at the station, but I didn't dare tell anyone what I had seen, because I'd have been sent to Rainhill mental hospital.'

After that night, Stan deliberately avoided looking too intently into the park on his beat, but a few times, always, around 4am, he would catch sight of something moving with lightning speed out of the corner of his eye as he passed Abercromby Park.

Perhaps the Thing in Abercromby Park is still at large today ...

In the summer of 1975, five-year-old Christopher was living with his parents Ken and Sue, and his twelve-year-old old sister Meg in a sixteen-storey block of ninety-one flats in Bootle, called Mersey House. One evening the boy was playing in his room when he heard a strange clicking sound coming from the wall near to the headboard of his bed. Christopher went and grabbed big sister Meg's hand and dragged her into the room and told her to listen too, but when she did, she heard nothing, as the clicks had stopped.

As soon as Meg left the room, the rapid ticking sound started again, so this time Christopher went into the living room to fetch his mother Sue. 'It's probably a clock ticking somewhere, love,' she suggested. 'These walls are like paper.' she carried on pouring a cup of tea for her father, Bill, who was, of course, Christopher's grandfather. Grand-dad always visited on Wednesdays, and loved playing with his grandson and telling him stories. When Bill heard Christopher mention the clicks, he said, 'Perhaps it's a death watch beetle; they make a ticking sound when they knock their head against the wood.'

Christopher giggled at the thought of a beetle butting its head against wood, but the boy's mother, who hated all bugs, shuddered, and said, 'Oh no! for goodness' sake, we haven't got death watch beetles have we? How big are they?'

At this moment, Christopher's father Ken came home from work and overheard the mention of the dreaded beetle. 'Death watch beetles? In this place?' Ken laughed sarcastically.

'Oh, it's possible,' said Bill, 'and they don't half cause some damage, you know.'

'This block of flats is practically brand new,' said Ken, taking his jacket off. 'You only get death watch beetles in old properties like churches and old houses. Mersey House is only seven years old.'

'They bang their heads against the wood, Dad,' Christopher excitedly told his father, and then with a frown, the boy went on, 'And there's one in my bedroom. Come and listen to it.'

'We haven't got death watch beetles in our flat, Christopher,' said Ken, in his condescending don't-talk-daft tone of voice, and he turned to Bill and said, 'What've you been filling his head with this time, Bill?'

'Hey,' Sue interposed, 'me dad hasn't been filling his head with anything; Christopher said he heard a clicking sound in his room, that's all.'

Ken sank into his armchair and shielded himself from the ridiculous conversation behind the large broadsheet *Liverpool Echo*.

That evening, after Christopher had been put to bed, he couldn't sleep because it was too warm, and he lay there looking at the ceiling, picturing a beetle knocking its shiny black globular head against the wall. He giggled to himself, and then turned on his side and eventually managed to doze off. Some time later, Christopher awoke, and looked over to the window. Now the sky was black, and although he couldn't yet tell the time, he knew it must be very late. It was, in fact three in the morning, and Christopher's sister and parents were all soundly asleep.

Then he heard those clicks again, and this time something happened that gave him a fright.

The lever-handle of his bedroom door slowly turned. Then the door opened some six or seven inches, so the light from the landing shone into Christopher's room. That landing light was always left on in case he wanted to go to the toilet during the night.

Christopher sat up in bed and with wide, frightened eyes looked at the door which had opened, seemingly all by itself. 'Is that you, Meg?' he asked, hoping his sister was playing a prank on him, but there was no reply.

Then he noticed the strange shoe on the floor, protruding from behind the door frame. Someone was standing on the landing to the right of that doorway, and they were wearing a long black pointed shoe, like the ones princes sometimes wore in fairy tales.

Then came the second shock. The silhouette of a long pointed nose slowly came into view, and it was so far up the doorframe, it obviously belonged to someone, or something, that was well above average height. This

155

really scared Christopher, and once again, he hoped someone, maybe his father, was messing about, even though he knew full well that his dad would never do anything as stupid as putting on pointed black shoes and wearing a false pointed nose in the middle of the night, and anyway, Christopher's father was only smallish, and this weird figure looked enormous. More out of nerves than curiosity, the little boy asked feebly, 'Who's that?'

That familiar clicking sound began again, only this time it didn't come from the wall next to Christopher's bed, it came from the sinister half-hidden figure.

'Mum!' Christopher shouted, at the top of his voice, and began to shiver all over. 'Mum! I don't like it!'

'Shut up!' snapped the creepy nocturnal visitor, and Christopher saw his nose twitch slightly as he spoke. 'If you shout out again, I'll come and get you.'

Christopher started crying, and the menacing figure warned, 'Stop your silly crying or I'll throw you out the window. Do you want me to throw you out?'

'Mum!' Christopher screamed as loudly as his lungs would allow this time, and the nose and the black foot darted silently away from the door. Seconds later, the boy's father came into the room, 'What's to do, son? Can't you sleep?'

Christopher couldn't stop crying long enough to tell his father. He sobbed and reached out for him with tears streaming from his eyes.

'It's okay, son, did you have a nightmare, hey?' Ken said, and embraced his little lad. Sue came into the room and said, 'Is he okay?'

'A man said he'd throw me out the window!' Christopher said between heavy sobs, and his mum stroked his head and said, 'There's no man here,

Christopher. You've had a bad dream, that's all.'

And even as she was reassuring him, Christopher saw the nose of the partially hidden entity suddenly poke out from behind the doorframe yet again. The child let out a scream and pointed to it, but before Ken and Sue had a chance to see it, the nose had flitted away again.

'I think he's got a bit of a temperature,' Sue reckoned, feeling her son's forehead with her palm.

'Do you want to sleep with mummy and daddy tonight?' Ken asked, but Christopher didn't reply because he was staring intently at the doorway in utter panic.

Ken picked the boy up and as he walked with him towards the door, Christopher screamed at the top of his voice and clung on to his father, because he expected to see the eerie figure waiting outside on the landing. He squeezed his eyes shut in case he saw him over his father's shoulder as Ken took him into the bedroom. Thankfully, the boy slept securely and soundly between his parents that night, but a few nights later, the ominous supernatural visitant returned, again at around three in the morning.

The boy was once again lying in bed, and this time the room was cooler because Sue had opened the top narrow window pane. The clicking sounds were heard again, only this time they went on for several minutes before that nose and pointed black shoe appeared in the doorway. This time, four long black fingers, much longer and thinner than normal human fingers, came sliding round the doorframe, tapping rapidly on the wood as they did so. Now Christopher knew exactly what was generating those clicks. 'I'll shout for my daddy if you don't go away!' he screamed.

'Your daddy's dead, and your mummy as well,' cackled the entity.

Christopher shouted for his mother at the top of his voice, but this time no one answered his cry for help. All of a sudden, Christopher felt he should pray to Jesus for help, and he stood up, placed his hands together, and closed his eyes as he had been taught by his mother. He was too young to know the Lord's Prayer, or any standard common prayer, but he had been told by his mum to turn to Jesus if he was ever in trouble. He screwed his eyes tightly shut and pleaded for help in his own childish way.

'Arrgh!' the strange being groaned as it heard the child whispering the ad hoc prayer, and its fingers, nose and pointed shoe withdrew again.

This time, it was Christopher's sister Meg who came into his room, and she switched on the light and threw her arms around him. 'Aww, did you just shout me, baby?' the girl asked with a loving smile to her 'baby brother' as she called him. 'Did you have another bad dream, Chrissy?' she said, and hugged him hard.

'That man said he killed mum and dad!' the boy shrieked, and burst into tears.

'Huh?' Meg gave a puzzled look, and then she shouted her mother. The girl tried to pick up Christopher, but found him too heavy, so she tried to drag him out of the bed. As she did so, she caught sight of the pointed black shoe and long nose peeping out from behind the doorframe. 'Who's that?' she cried.

At the mere sight of that long nose Christopher became hysterical and wrestled free of his sister and dived under the bed sheets.

For what seemed like an eternity, Meg sat on the bed cradling her brother in her arms in a state of terror, only too well aware of the partially-revealed lanky fiend standing there on the landing. She screamed and screamed for her mother and father, but they never came.

Eventually the figure moved away from the door, and Meg dared to take a chance. She dragged a screaming, kicking Christopher from the bedroom and into their parent's room. Sue and Ken were both lying on their backs with their pillows covering their faces. Were they dead? Meg crept towards the two figures, silent as corpses, and gingerly removed the pillows from their faces, terrified lest the evil intruder had smothered them, but as soon as she had removed the pillows they began to stir. Disorientated at first, it was as if they had both been drugged, or put under some kind of hypnosis. Neither could explain how they had got into that situation.

Enough was enough. Sue had always claimed she was partially psychic, or 'sikey' as she called her paranormal faculty, and, in addition to the strange goings on, she was getting a strong sense that there was something evil abroad in the house and that it was no longer safe for them to stay there. She suggested staying over at her father's house in Litherland for a week. Ken said that was a ridiculous idea. He also reminded Sue that he was getting up for work in a few hours, and he needed his sleep. But Sue went with her instincts and took herself and the children to her dad's house, even though it caused a blazing row and she felt uneasy about leaving Ken alone in the house.

On the following day, a terrific explosion erupted in one of the ground-floor flats in Mersey House, and it was so powerful, it damaged the other ninety-one flats in the high-rise block, injuring thirty-two people. The janitor, a Mr Saunderson, was badly injured by the blast, which was thought to have been caused by a gas leakage.

Earlier that summer, police had uncovered a cache of weapons belonging to the IRA at a residence just a few miles from Mersey House, so Special Branch were instantly informed when news of the blast was reported. Some 250 residents in the block were made homeless by the incident, but luckily, Ken was visiting his wife Sue and children at the time of the explosion, and the family were later rehoused into a lovely house on Rimrose Valley Road, Crosby.

Christopher is a grown man now with a family of his own, and Meg is married and living in London with two children. Even today, brother and sister remember that mysterious evil figure that hid outside Christopher's bedroom door, and Christopher and Meg suspect that the entity was some sort of omen connected to the gas explosion that damaged Mersey House that summer in 1975.

The death watch beetle received its name because its clicks were thought to be an omen of an impending death, and it's strange how the 'bogeyman' seen by Christopher and Meg also produced similar clicks before a catastrophic tragedy befell Mersey House, so perhaps the mysterious intruder was some sort of omen.

The following story has played on my mind, haunted me, in fact, for many years, since it was first told to me back in 1996. I managed, through a radio station, to get in touch with several people involved in the story, including a taxi driver. It is a difficult story to put into words. See what you think.

Bobby and Joe, two twelve-year-old boys, were messing about one evening and foolishly clung on to the back of a heavy-goods lorry and somehow managed to hang on without being seen until the vehicle was trundling along the East Lancashire Road near Windle, just north of St Helens. It was here that a vigilant police motorcyclist spotted them and flagged the driver down. Bobby and Joe were taken back home in disgrace and were severely reprimanded by their parents that night, and grounded for almost a week.

A fortnight later though, the adventurous pair were roaming far from home again, and this time they wandered nine miles through the streets of the city until they ended up at Garston Docks. Here, something very peculiar took place that would have far-reaching implications. Bobby and Joe were walking along Dock Road, which leads, as its name suggests, from one of the Garston docks. The time was 3.40pm, and they were passing three run-down terraced houses, when they saw a man standing stock-still on the other side of the road, staring at them. This man, who was aged between thirty-five and forty and over six feet in height, was dressed in a black suit, and looked very outdated for the mid-1970s, because his trousers were not flared, but straight, and his jet-black hair was short and slicked back. His equally black moustache contrasted sharply with his pale white skin. He wore a white shirt and a black tie, and his shoes were also black. Even from across the road, the boys noticed this out of vogue stranger had prominent thick black eyebrows, which gave his face a brooding appearance. Bobby pulled a face at the man, but Joe, nervously sensing that the man was 'not right in the head', told him to stop taunting him.

The stranger then crossed the road and walked towards them. Bobby yelped and pretended to laugh before running off, and Joe bolted off close behind him, disturbed by the odd-looking man. The children slowed down when they got to St Mary's Road, but the man was still following them. They speeded up again and ran as far as they could before they were both suffering from nagging stitches in their sides, and when they looked back down Aigburth Road, they were relieved to see that the eerie pursuer was now just a black spot in the distance.

At one point he seemed to stop, and the boys watched him turn left down a side street named Stratford Road. At that moment the skies darkened, and thunder rolled across the low clouds. It started to rain. Bobby and Joe sought refuge from the pelting rain under a deserted bus shelter. Lightning flashed, startling the young lads and the rain was soon torrenting down so heavily it was hard to see through it. Yet there was some foolish person walking in the downpour, and then it gradually dawned on the lads who it was.

In dread they watched the dark figure approaching from Horringford Road; the stalker from Garston, still on their trail. He had crept up on them from the other direction by taking a devious route down two streets off the main thoroughfare.

Bobby and Joe fled from the bus stop into the bucketing rain, rushing across the road in blind panic. A bus, horn blaring, hurtled past them, throwing up a wave of rainwater from the gutter over Bobby's shorts. The two boys, sodden to the skin, ran up to the first person they saw, a rather austere-looking gentleman of about fifty in a navy blue raincoat and flat cap, 'There's a man chasing us!' Bobby cried.

'He's out to get us!' panted Joe.

'Well you must have done something wrong then,' the man replied, and tugged at the peak of his cap in the torrent of rain and brought the lapels of his coat together with a giant fist.

'That's him there!' shouted Joe, pointing out the man in black to the passer-by, but he was not interested in being a good Samaritan and just bowed his head to the slanting rain and walked on his way.

The boys ran up Ashfield Road with dazzling forks of lightning streaking down from the darkening skies, and soon they were so out of breath, they could hardly utter a word as they tried to cross Sefton Park. Not once did they actually see their sinister pursuer as they traversed the park, yet they imagined him hiding behind every tree and bush. By the time they had reached Smithdown Road, they were ready to drop from exhaustion. A kind taxi driver noticed Joe sitting on the pavement, crying, with Bobby kneeling beside him, trying to pull him to his feet. The cabby asked the boys where they lived and each gave an address in the West Derby area, off Muirhead Avenue East. 'Okay, muckers. Get in,' he said.

Inside the cab, as the rain clattered on the vehicle's roof, Joe was giving a rambling description of the man in black when, suddenly, Bobby tremblingly pointed beyond the rain-streaked offside passenger window. 'That's him, over there, look!'

'Oh, is it now?' the cabby said, and jumped out of the taxi, locked the boys in, and went to confront the weird stalker who had followed the children for miles. The man in the black suit and thick black eyebrows darted down an alleyway, and the cabby chased after him. Joe and Bobby shivered inside the taxi in their wet clothes for what seemed like half an hour, though only ten minutes had in fact elapsed, when they heard a knocking on the side of the taxi.

It was the stalker, and his eyes narrowed as they fixed on the terror-stricken children. From close range his vacant eyes seemed devoid of life. He was obviously insane, yet like most people who are afflicted with madness, he was cunning, and after trying the locked passenger door, he went to the driver's window, which was partly wound down, and inserted his pale slender-fingered hand through the narrow gap in an effort to release the lock. He managed to unfasten the driver's door and was about to get into the taxi when the cabby returned and threw a powerful punch into the weirdo's back, which was so violent it shook the vehicle.

With the two boys trembling in the back seat, the taxi driver and the stalker fell out of the cab as they grappled with one another in the gutter, which had now become a river. The cabby, who although only medium height, was stocky and obviously knew how to defend himself. He ended up delivering an upper-cut to the creepy stranger's jaw, which laid him flat on his back. The taxi driver then jumped into his cab and drove off to West Derby, sucking the grazed knuckles of his left hand now and then.

The driver kept asking the boys if they had any idea who the man was, but they could only repeat that they didn't have a clue. Bobby didn't dare admit that he had probably provoked the whole incident by pulling faces at the stalker. He kept looking out of the rear window, expecting to see the figure following the taxi, but when the cab pulled into the road where he lived, Bobby felt safe at last and a new preoccupation began to trouble him – dealing with his parents – who would be furious at him for gallivanting far from home yet again. The taxi driver escorted Bobby to the front door, and told his parents about the unbalanced man who had followed him and his friend from Garston, all the way to Smithdown Road, and advised them to contact the police.

'Eee dear, this one has caused so much lumber,' Bobby's father told the caring cabby. 'Thanks very much, mate for looking after them. Lord knows what would've happened to them if you hadn't picked them up.'

Bobby's mother threw her arms around him, and feeling he was soaked to the skin, promptly marched him and Joe to the bathroom and told them to dry themselves off while she brought them some dry clothes.

Three days after this, Bobby went into his backyard one evening at the behest of his mother, to put a carrier bag full of rubbish into the dustbin. As he was replacing the bin lid, he heard a gentle rap-rap-rapping on the backyard gate, and thinking it was his grandfather, who often knocked on that gate in the evening when he dropped by (much to the annoyance of Bobby's mother, who would have to cook something extra for her father-in-law). Sometimes grand-dad also brought his friend Mick with him, and on those evenings Bobby's mother always went through the roof, because Mick would usually try and cadge cigarettes off her, and he had a terrible body odour problem.

Bobby slid back the bolt and was just about to open the back gate when he had a frightening premonition. Something told him the late night caller might not be his grandfather, but the uncanny stalker. Before he could slide the bolt back on, the lever of the gate handle tilted and the door opened about five inches and long white manicured fingers slid round the edge of it.

Bobby backed away and almost tripped over the dustbin. He tried to cry out for his parents but he couldn't raise his voice above a whisper, as his throat had seemingly closed up.

The stalker silently edged round the gate and into the yard and with the dead-pan expression that made him seem even more terrifying, he walked towards Bobby, who had backed into a corner. There was no escape. His entire body was now paralysed with fear. The menacing stranger halted about three feet away and gazed down at the boy with his ghastly inhuman eyes. A raspy-sounding voice, that seemed to originate in the air near to the lunatic's left shoulder, rather than from his mouth said, 'Kill him!'

Bobby felt faint as he saw the stranger's lily-white hands reach out, convinced he was about to be strangled.

In the nick of time, in through the back door came Bobby's grandfather and his freeloading friend Mick, laughing and chatting on their way back from the pub.

'Grand-dad!' Bobby screamed at last.

'Hiya, lad,' the boy's grandfather said, then saw the stranger, and challenged him. 'Hey! You! What's your game?'

The pallid madman turned to face Bobby's grandfather

and Mick, and then Bobby's father came out of the house via the kitchen door, wondering why his son was taking so long to put a small bag of rubbish into the bin.

'Dad!' Bobby yelled from the corner of the yard, 'That's the fellah who kept following me and Joe!'

Suddenly finding courage now that his father and grandfather had come to the rescue, Bobby then lifted the dustbin lid, leaped upwards with it, and hit the baleful man on the back of the head with it. There was a resounding clang as the lid struck his skull, and yet he remained standing, unmoved. Bobby's father was not a great fighter, by any means, but he picked up one of his wife's potted plants in its terracotta pot and hurled it at the ominous figure, and the pot smashed against his face, but the soil sprayed out all over the place and some of it hit Mick in the eyes. Mick stumbled back against the backyard wall, complaining he had been blinded. The stalker suddenly turned and glared at Bobby, who was cowering in the corner again, then turned and bolted out of the yard. Bobby's father and grandfather tried to give chase, but the agile mystery man managed to escape into the night.

Not until two in the morning, when grandfather and Mick had left the house, could Bobby be persuaded to go to bed. He lay back, with the bedside light on, but kept imagining he could see the silhouette of his demonic pursuer at the window. Despite his fears, he eventually began to feel drowsy and was just drifting off when the wardrobe door emitted a long creaking sound. He froze, and shouted for his father, but his father did not respond. A second creak. The door had opened by itself, only an inch or two, but there was an index finger protruding from inside the wardrobe! He must be in there! The stalker was in the house and somehow had got into the wardrobe! Bobby screamed, and sat up in a sweat. A mere three minutes had elapsed since he had dozed off. His heart was beating like a bass drum. He looked again at the wardrobe. This time the door was thankfully firmly closed.

The man in black was seen one more time, in the middle of one gloomy afternoon when Bobby was in the school playground. He suddenly noticed the familiar figure standing in the street outside, staring directly at him through the school railings with that gloomy poker-faced expression and those creepy, lifeless eyes. Bobby ran to fetch a teacher, but by the time he had brought her to the railings, he was nowhere to be seen.

After that day, the stalker was seen no more, but for many years, Bobby suffered terrible nightmares about the weird character, imagining him hiding in every crevice and around every corner.

When I told this story on the radio some few years ago, I received a letter and three emails from four listeners who had also been stalked by a man whose description matched that of the stalker who terrorised Bobby and his friend in 1975.

One woman named Val, told me how, in June 1970, as a sixteen-year-old girl, she had boarded a Number 3 bus to her home in Walton from the Pier Head terminus after a day out with her friends. Halfway through the journey she felt a hand stroking her long blonde hair. She turned and saw a man aged about thirty-eight with a black moustache, strange staring eyes and prominent thick black eyebrows, sitting behind her. He was dressed in a black suit and wore a black tie. She told him to stop touching her hair and the bus conductor also ordered the man to 'behave' or he'd be escorted off the vehicle.

When Val reached her destination in Walton she got as far as Rice Lane, before noticing that the man who had sat behind her playing with her hair was now following her to her home on Grey Road. She estimated his height to be at least six feet two inches, which made him seem even more intimidating.

For the following three weeks, the peculiar man in black followed her to and from the city centre, where she worked in the Kardomah tea factory. On one occasion Val woke up early one morning to find him standing at the foot of her bed. She was so afraid she dived under the blankets, and when she was forced to uncover her face for fear of suffocation, she could still see the stranger standing motionless in a dark corner of the room, barely visible in the faint morning light. She screamed, and moments later she and her brother heard footsteps on the stairs, followed by the slamming of the front door. A neighbour on his way to work early that morning said he had seen a smartly-dressed man in a black suit enter Val's house with a key, but had assumed it was some relative of the family, so had thought nothing more of it at the time.

The description of the second stalker, black plastered down hair, black moustache, black suit, black tie and white shirt, seems to suggest these incidents are the work of the same creepy individual.

The next incident was in Speke, and the year was 1977. Twenty-two-year-old Felicity was sitting watching television at her home one summer evening when she caught a sudden movement out of the corner of her eye. She turned slowly, and caught a glimpse of a man's face peeping in at her through the window that overlooks her back garden. The man had jet-black hair, black moustache, and 'mad staring eyes'. This Peeping Tom was evidently obsessed with Felicity, for on several occasions when she paid evening visits to her friend Kerry in Halewood, over a mile away, the pale-faced stalker would be seen peering through the living room window there as well. Each time he appeared, Kerry's father would rush outside to try and catch the audacious voyeur, but he was never fast enough and the stalker would inexplicably have vanished. This stalking mystery went on for almost a year, then ended as mysteriously as it had begun.

There were two other similar cases reported to me, both involving a stalker who matches the descriptions in the previous accounts. A Wavertree woman named Margaret in her late forties, told me how, from 1989 to 1991, she would often catch glimpses of a man dressed in a black suit, with combed back hair that looked Brylcreemed, sneaking about in her home off Wavertree Road. Right from the beginning, Margaret was in no doubt that the man was a ghost, and even asked a psychic friend to make contact with the apparition. The entity communicated with her and saying he was a 'Mr Mann' who had taken his own life a long time ago, but would not provide any further information. The medium then sketched the face of the ghost and it was that of a man with a heavy black moustache, combed back coal-black hair and dark eyes. Mr Mann subsequently admitted he had followed other people around, and that he had not died in the Wavertree house Margaret had lived in, but had taken his life at a house in Garston.

Besides Margaret, three other people saw the ghost in her home, including two friends who saw the reflection of a man they could not account for in the television screen one evening. They could plainly see their own reflections in the screen, but they could not explain the presence of another reflection, that of a man in a black suit, or perhaps a tuxedo, who was not in the room. After a while the phantom reflection faded away.

In 2008 I received an email from another woman who may have received unwanted attention from the ubiquitous Mr Mann. In March 2007, twenty-year-old Amy started dating Simon, a student, who lived on Island Road, Garston. One evening, Amy left her home in Allerton and walked to her boyfriend's home, and as she passed under a bridge, she became aware of a man following her. She turned and saw he was dressed in a black suit, with a white shirt and a dark-coloured tie, possibly black. He looked to be about thirty-five to forty, and was at least six feet tall. Every time Amy passed under that bridge on her way to Simon's home, the same man in black would appear and then lie in wait for her and then follow her all the way to her boyfriend's house. This happened on about eight occasions, until Amy decided it would be better for her nerves if Simon came to see her instead of her going to see him.

Many ghosts of this sort are earthbound spirits that merely continue to carry out the same routines and exhibit the same behaviour patterns they enacted when they were alive, and yet I feel this explanation does not apply to the 'Mister Mann' ghost. There is more to him than meets the eye. We may unravel the mystery one day.

171

Who is the greatest bogeyman of them all? Well, the Devil is much too superior in his dark work to be termed a mere bogeyman, but as a figure of fear and fascination, he is unequalled across this world, and that goes for Liverpool too ...

Legend has it that there are specific places in the North West where people should go to sell their soul to the Devil. Most of these meeting places are at crossroads, the traditional rendezvous point, but bridges also feature in the gazetteer of the damned, and for many years, the bridge on Rose Lane, which spans the railway tracks leading to and from Mossley Hill station, has had an infamous association with Satanic soul exchanges.

In the late 1950s a Woolton businessman surnamed James lost all of his life savings in a catastrophic business venture, and considered blowing his brains out in Sefton Park with a pistol. Accordingly, he wrote a suicide note to his estranged wife before setting out for the park with his army service revolver. He found a secluded spot, sat down, and went over in his mind the events that had led him to this moment. Having decided that he had nothing left to live for, he put the gun to his head but couldn't bring himself to pull the trigger. Something was stopping him. So he left the park and aimlessly wandered the streets until he came to the Rose of Mossley pub, at the junction of Rose Lane and Bridge Road, in the Mossley Hill district of Liverpool.

In the pub Mr James overheard a curious conversation between two old men about a certain local soldier who had come home after the Second World War to find that his wife had abandoned him. Not only that, the soldier soon became seriously ill, and ended up being diagnosed with a virulent form of tuberculosis. His condition worsened, and he went to 'the bridge' at midnight to sell his soul to the Devil. The Devil duly appeared, and in exchange for the soldier's soul, gave him twenty more years of excellent health and great fortune. According to the old chap telling the story, the soldier was now a wealthy businessman, living in Caldy.

Mr James went over to the table where the two old men were sitting. 'I couldn't help overhearing your story about the soldier just then,' he admitted, 'and I was wondering which bridge it was that you were talking about.'

The old men quickly tried to retract what they had said, saying the story was just a bit of nonsense – mere hearsay and rumour – but Mr James still pressed them into revealing the location of the bridge. One of the old men took him to the door of the Rose of Mossley and pointed to the infamous rendezvous-point. 'Over there, that's it,' said the old man, indicating the slight bump in the road which formed the bridge across the railway tracks. 'Nothing much to look at, is it?'

Mr James lingered around the area until midnight, and then he stood on the bridge, waiting for the Devil to make an appearance, but no one showed up. 'If you can hear me, give me a sign,' Mr James whispered, 'because I want to do a deal with you. Make me rich again for twenty years and you can have my soul in return. I solemnly mean what I say.'

Just then a little mongrel dog came trotting along the bridge and stopped a few feet away from Mr James, who suspected the animal might be the Devil in disguise. 'Is it you?' he asked the dog, and it barked furiously at the failed businessman.

Then the shadow of a man's head and shoulders slid across the wall of the bridge, and Mr James turned to see what the dog was barking at. It was the silhouette of a man with horns, but he was well over average height. He estimated the entity's height to be at least six feet five inches. He wore a long black coat that reached down to his knees, and his dark green shoes looked like turned up Persian slippers.

The wide staring eyes radiated pure menace, but his rich deep voice was strangely enticing as it offered him a stark choice: 'Twenty years of wealth I shall give to you in return for your soul. Do you agree to these terms?'

Mr James was trembling now, but he managed a nod, at which, the mongrel bolted off across the bridge into the night.

'Then say you agree to them!' the Devil prompted him.

'I agree to these terms,' said Mr James, but his voice

was barely audible because his throat had closed up as the magnitude of what he was saying had begun to penetrate his troubled brain.

'So be it! And then I shall collect what is mine.'

In a flash, the Devil then spun round, but the moment his back was presented to Mr James, he vanished instantly. An acrid aroma, reminiscent of charred pork, filled the air and he was left alone on the bridge to contemplate the enormity of what he had just done.

Overnight, Mr James's fortunes reversed. Three days after the deal was struck with the Devil, he received an unexpected windfall when his premium bonds were chosen by Ernie, the electronic random number generator at Lytham St Annes, in Lancashire. His wife soon returned to him, and after taking her out for a meal one night, they went, on a whim, to a bingo hall, where he won £400.

With the capital he had acquired he was able to invest in a scrap metal business and made so much money he sold this business a year later for a fortune and then ventured into the property market. Mr James prospered in every sphere of business, and was either envied or admired by his rivals. Another businessman who had been orchestrating a groundless smear campaign against him, involving falsified documents, died in a horrific car crash, and another man who tried to set fire to a factory belonging to Mr James accidentally burnt himself to death. Mr James confided to his best friend that his outstanding success in all fields was due to his having sold his soul to the Devil, and he advised him to follow in his footsteps. His friend was shocked and appalled by what he had heard and quickly abandoned him, despite having been his loyal friend since childhood.

The story goes, that in the late 1970s, twenty years

175

after making his pact with the Devil, Mr James lost his wife, and then one by one, his businesses went bankrupt. His health went into a rapid decline, and Mr James was only too well aware of what was happening to him. Realising he was in the direst of predicaments, he intended to turn to Jesus, fearing his time was up and that the Devil would soon be calling to collect his soul.

His next piece of bad luck was a heart attack and as the ambulance taking him to Sefton General passed over the very bridge in Mossley Hill where the diabolical deal had been struck twenty years before, a strange gloom filled the interior of the ambulance. Mr James's eyes bulged in terror and he never made it to the hospital. He was declared dead on arrival at Sefton General.

~

There is another hoary old tale of a young hopeless musician who sold his soul to the Devil on the same bridge. In December 1960, so this tale goes, John Lennon, then aged twenty, had heard the weird rumours about the 'Devil's Bridge' and became obsessed with the idea of selling his soul to Beelzebub in return for fame and fortune. His main aim was to be bigger than his idol, and rival, Elvis Presley – a performer who had ironically been accused of being in league with the Devil by playing the fiend's music – rock 'n' roll.

Lennon sneaked out of his house, at 251 Menlove Avenue, where he was living with his Aunt Mimi, and walked just over a mile through the December snow to the bridge of destiny, arriving there just before midnight. The Devil duly appeared as a tall shadowy figure with horns and the same uncanny-looking eyes, as described by Mr James. A bargain was struck. Within three years, millions upon millions of people would idolise Lennon, and the rest of his band – The Beatles. They would smash all sales records with their songs, and their success would be unprecedented. The band would be seemingly surrounded by an aura that caused the youth of the day to erupt into an ecstatic frenzy known as Beatlemania (a term first coined by Professor Rex Makin, a close friend of Beatles manager Brian Epstein).

Then there were the curious digs John Lennon had at Christianity and Jesus and his disciples. In 1966, Lennon quipped that the Beatles were now bigger than Christ and he called Jesus's disciples 'thick'. 'Christianity will go,' he told a reporter. 'It will vanish and shrink. I needn't argue about that. I'm right and will be proved right. We're more popular than Jesus now.'

Around this time, a musician who was in awe of the global following enjoyed by the Beatles asked John how he could account for his stratospheric success, and the reply he received was probably tongue in cheek: 'I sold my soul to the Devil,' John told him calmly – but was this really just one of those throw-away remarks that John was famous for?

Personally, I believe the Beatles' success can be explained through a number of mundane factors. They were an exceedingly skilful ensemble of musicians who had gone through a rigorous apprenticeship with their gruelling sessions in Hamburg, and both Lennon and McCartney were truly phenomenal songwriters (as Harrison was too in later years, when he was given a chance to shine). Brian Epstein was an extraordinary manager who played an important part in shaping the popular image of the Fab Four, and George Martin was nothing short of a genius producer – a true fifth Beatle, in fact. Then the timing was right. The Sixties era itself was the other hidden ingredient which set the stage for the revolutionary music of the Beatles. Without a doubt, there was a mass change in the collective consciousness of the planet at the beginning of that momentous decade. The Beatles' music was like nothing that had ever been heard before. Lennon once said, 'Before Elvis, there was nothing,' but many Beatles fans the world over would say that before the Beatles there was nothing; that popular music before the coming of the Fab Four was a wasteland, and some believe that the popular music scene has returned to a state of stagnancy in recent times.

Still the dark legend of Lennon's pact with the Devil continues to do the rounds. Some who believe in the story will cite strange incidents that seem to suggest that there was some supernatural genesis of the Beatles. Take, for example, the cryptic onstage remark John Lennon made after the death of his best friend, artist Stuart Sutcliffe, on Wednesday, 11 April 1962. John told the audience in Hamburg: 'Stuart Sutcliffe was a very special human being and a remarkable man. He once told me that he had the ability to see into the future and I for one now believe that Stu was telling the truth.'

What had happened to convince Lennon that Sutcliffe had the gift of premonition? There were rumours that Sutcliffe had told John Lennon that the Beatles would be bigger than anyone – even Elvis. Sutcliffe had, however possibly predicted that he would never see that success, for he would tragically die, aged twenty-one, from bleeding in the right ventricle of his brain.

The legend of the Faustian pact between Lennon and the fallen angel ends with the world-famous rock-star being gunned down outside the Dakota Apartments on the night of 8 December 1980 – exactly twenty years after the deal with the Devil, when the two decades of world fame and super-fortune had expired.

If John Lennon had really sold his soul to the Devil, why on earth was he a committed campaigner for world peace during his lifetime? Furthermore, I would imagine that people who had given their souls to Satan would not be able to return from Hell to be seen as ghosts after death, but there have been many consistent reports made to me, and other paranormal investigators, of John Lennon's ghost being seen across the city since his physical death in 1980. Most of these sightings are of Lennon in his prime, dressed in the iconic white suit we associate with the Abbey Road record cover. Many of the sightings centre around Mendips, Lennon's home on Menlove Avenue from the age of five, until the age of twenty-three, when world fame beckoned. Several of the sightings have been of John with a woman identified by some as his beloved Aunt Mimi.

In 1998, Woolton man Frank Johnson told me that he was walking his dog along Beaconsfield Road, just around the corner from Mendips, when his pet suddenly crouched down on the pavement and refused to budge. This was at 9.45pm on a summer's evening at the gates of Strawberry Field, immortalised in the 1967 Lennon and McCartney song. Frank happened to look beyond the red gates of the former orphanage, and there was a man who was unmistakably John Lennon, with his trademark NHS spectacles, long hair, but clean-shaven, and looking about thirty. He wore a white suit and stood there with his arms folded, gazing at Frank with a bemused look.

Standing next to Lennon's ghost was a woman who

looked as if she was in her fifties, or perhaps older, but she turned away and said something that Frank couldn't make out. Frank was so afraid, he picked up his dog – an overfed Labrador – and carried him quickly away from that poorly lit stretch of Beaconsfield Road. When he got home, he said to his wife, 'I've just seen a ghost in Strawberry Field.' He expected Linda to doubt his words, but instead she looked at him with a sombre expression and said, 'I've seen two of them a few times. Did he have a white suit on?'

Frank was flabbergasted. He had been a Beatles fan in his youth, but his wife, being in her late twenties, had never really been that interested in the Beatles, and had not recognised Lennon's ghost. Linda said she had seen the ghost walk straight through the closed gates of Strawberry Field a fortnight back, but had said nothing, as she had been brought up to believe that only bad luck would result from talking about such things. About a month before that, Linda had seen the man in the white suit reading graffiti (left by Beatles fans) on the stone gateposts of Strawberry Field, and when she walked past with the dog, he had vanished before her eyes.

These are just a couple of the many sightings of Lennon's ghost, but I have a folder bulging with other reports of the murdered Beatle's alleged spectre, in locations ranging from Gambier Terrace (where John lived in his art school days with Stuart Sutcliffe) to Old Hall Street, where the ghost was seen in the 1990s, as Paul McCartney was giving a concert at the King's Dock.

Still, the legends of the Devil's trading post on the Mossley Hill bridge and the tales of the souls for sale continue to be reported.

A few years ago I talked to a man named Mike Gilbert who told me how he had once seen the Devil on the bridge in question whilst taking a midnight walk during a bout of insomnia. At first, Mike thought the man, dressed in a black suit and black polo neck sweater, looked familiar, but he couldn't place him. The man passed Mike and bowed his head to look at the ground as they both walked along the bridge on Rose Lane. 'How do I know him?' Mike muttered faintly as he walked on, and looked back over his shoulder at the stranger, who was now also looking back. Mike walked on, and kept getting tantalising, fragmentary recollections of the stranger's face – and then, all of a sudden, he shuddered as he recalled just who he was.

In the 1970s, when Mike was a young man, he had been desperately in love with a woman whom he, (and many others), had regarded as the most beautiful girl in all of Liverpool – a red-head named Layla, and one evening a friend of Mike's tipped him off that Layla was a regular at Bailey's nightclub in St John's Precinct, so off Mike went, reeking of Aramis after-shave, with his long black hair freshly permed, as was the fashion.

Layla positively smouldered as she took to the dance floor in Bailey's and one girl was so jealous of the attention she was getting she tried to elbow her in the face, making out it was an accident, but was then ejected from the premises. Mike wasn't a bad dancer, but because he was so infatuated with Layla, he was scared of putting a foot wrong, which made him look clumsy and awkward. He danced as close to her as he dared, and she

181

started to notice him. She looked even more perfect at close quarters, and then suddenly a suave foreign-looking man danced between them, and literally whisked the beautiful Layla off her feet. The stranger moved with the perfection and energy of a Broadway dancer, and soon, everyone in Bailey's stopped dancing, and a circle of awestruck inferior-feeling clubgoers looked on as the tall dark stranger held Layla by her tiny waist, and started to swing her round.

Round and round the couple went, until, all of a sudden, the gyrations took on an unreal quality, for the dancers seemed to defy gravity. They twirled around with expressions of utter pleasure on their faces, until they were a blur. The circle backed away, sensing the 'foreigner' was someone very unearthly.

'Look! Their feet aren't even touching the ground!' Mike's friend, Arthur cried above the music. 'How the heck are they doing it?'

The music stopped, but the duo were still spinning round so fast, they were actually making a humming sound and generating a breeze. A teenaged girl looking on fainted, sensing that the extraordinary gravity-defying dancer was the Devil, and then the couple slowly stopped spinning and their feet landed gently back on the dance floor.

A lad called Paul, who was one of the many red-blooded males who had his own designs on Layla, stepped forward, intending to roughly grab the ultra-talented unknown dancer by his arm, but smoke was seen to come off Paul's sizzling hand the minute he touched the stranger's arm. The foreigner laughed as Paul quickly withdrew his hand and cried out in pain, 'Ouch! He's hot!'

182

As Layla sank to her knees, then collapsed on the dance floor, her extraordinarily-skilled dancing partner strutted across the floor and disappeared into the toilets. Paul and Mike followed him, and a few other men also went after him out of curiosity, thinking there would be a fight, but upon entering the gents toilets, Mike and Paul found that the he had vanished, despite there being no possible exit.

Layla never went to Bailey's nightclub after that night, nor any of the other clubs she used to frequent, and no one ever heard from her again. That was over thirty years ago and now, here was that same man standing before Mike on the bridge. Long ago Mike had reasoned that the dancer must have been the Devil, and now here he was again looking exactly the same; he had not aged a day.

Mike hurried home, terrified that the Devil might be following him, and on reaching his house, he told his wife a garbled version of the story of Layla, and how he had just seen the same man she had danced with before she vanished. Mike's wife, Lorna, shook her head, and said, 'Why would the Devil want to dance with a girl in a Liverpool nightclub? And what would he be doing out walking on a cold night in Mossley Hill? He could dance with any of the world's supermodels, in places like Monte Carlo, or Paris, so why would he choose boring old Mossley Hill?'

'How do I know? I just know what I saw, and I didn't like it, okay?'

Mike took a warm bath before bedtime in an effort to unwind, because his insomnia was making him feel depressed and run down of late. As he sat rubbing one of Lorna's fragrant bars of herbal-based soap on his upper arm, he started to hum a tune, without even realising it.

He was beginning to question whether the stranger on the bridge had merely looked like that weird dancer from thirty years ago, who had literally tripped the light fantastic in Bailey's. Surely it was too incredible to be true. The bar of soap suddenly slipped out of his hand and fell into the bath with a plop. He leaned forward, about to search for it, when a hand came out of the bath water and handed him the mislaid bar of soap. Mike recoiled in horror, and almost dived out of the bath. He ran jibbering from the bathroom and told Lorna what had just happened.

'Hey! Steady on! You need to get a grip, love,' she said and went into the bathroom. She pulled the plug out of the bath and stood there smiling until the water had nearly all gone. 'Nope, there's no one in here,' she laughed, retrieving the bar of soap from the last few inches of bath-water.

Mike wouldn't even come into the bathroom, but stood naked and shivering in the doorway, staring at the emptying bath. And then his eyes wandered to the steamed-up wall-mirror over the wash basin and the enormous hand-print on it. No ordinary hand-print, for all the fingers were all the same length. Lorna saw it too. 'Oh my God!' she cried, all her scepticism suddenly gone.

And then there came a low moaning voice from the last dregs of the bath-water as it disappeared down the plug-hole. 'L-o-r-n-a!' the voice said three times with great clarity, after which Lorna could not stop screaming for almost half an hour.

The couple were so traumatised by their encounter with what they believed to be the Devil, that they joined a prayer group at a local church, and up to now, there have been no further devilish goings-on at their home.

THE BLACK ELVES OF BLOODY ACRE

This is a very puzzling tale that has never been satisfactorily explained. It concerns one George Winter Warr, who was the Vicar of Childwall, at All Saints Church, from 1870 until his death at the age of eighty-one in 1895. Reverend Warr was known for his fire and brimstone sermons, many of which were addressed specifically at the drinkers of the parish, because Warr was a strict teetotaller.

In September 1874, there was nothing short of an epidemic of drunkenness in Liverpool, which spurred on the self-righteous reverend to increase his efforts to reform his parishioners. No one was spared, and he aimed one of his firebrand sermons at several professional parishioners, including a doctor, and a local police detective, whom he accused of drinking on duty.

Facing All Saints Church, there was, and still is, a beautiful old pub called the Childwall Abbey Hotel, but our reverend deemed this drinking establishment to be too near the church for his liking. Whenever Warr he walked past the pub, Warr would look through the latticed windows to glare and fume at the 'sinners' within, and the parishioners enjoying a drink in the Childwall Abbey would turn guiltily away.

One Sunday, in the spring of 1874, Warr delivered a damning sermon, in which he actually named the Childwall Abbey pub as a den of iniquity, and he told the congregation: 'When the wine is in, the wit is out! Bacchus [the god of wine and alcoholic beverages in general] has drowned more men in this town than Neptune!'

On the following Wednesday, an anonymous letter, obviously penned by some prankster with the design of invoking a reaction, was received by the fanatical vicar. It read:

Your Holiness,

You are forever condemning the drinkers of your parish, but people close to you know you're but a hypocrite of the worst type, and we know you've emptied many a bottle of wine behind closed doors after Mass. Your fine words dress ill deeds! Pretended holiness is a double iniquity, and there is no rogue like the Godly rogue! You live off the very people you condemn, but you're quick enough to pass the basket among us, aren't you? You're like a fox in the pulpit, preaching to the geese!
He who buys land buys many stones, he who buys meat buys many bones, and he who buys eggs buys

many shells – but he who is wise enough to buy good
ale, buys nothing else.

May the Lord reveal your many sins to the parish,

(signed) One Who Tells the Truth

Instead of ignoring the anonymous letter, the vicar became so enraged by its contents, he left his house and stormed into the Childwall Abbey pub, which was only playing host to a handful of drinkers at that time, and most of them were farmhands slaking their thirst at noon after a heavy morning in the fields. Few of them were literate enough to write their own names, never mind pen a vitriolic letter of such savage criticism. Warr ranted and raved and promised eternal damnation for the 'faceless coward' who had written the poison pen letter, but his bombastic accusations were met only by blank stares and bemused expressions from the bumpkins.

One Sunday evening in the late summer of that year, at around 9pm, an Irishman named Michael Maloney came stumbling into the pub, his face as white as a sheet, and his hands trembling as he placed his money on the bar. He said he'd just 'seen things' across the road in a field adjacent to the graveyard of All Saints Church. Maloney had foolishly taken a short-cut across 'the Acre' as the locals called it. This was a mysterious acre of land that had always been left uncultivated, because of an ancient law that strictly prohibited its use. Weeds, brambles and wild flowers run rampant there, even today. Some call this field the Bloody Acre, but no local historian can tell you why. Even Romany people travelling through Childwall have refused to camp upon the Bloody Acre. Perhaps the gypsies, with their well-reported powers of clairvoyance, can sense something very unsavoury about the field.

Everyone in the pub urged the Irishman to tell what he had seen, but he just kept repeating, 'I couldn't describe 'em, and I'm too scared to say what I seen, in case they comes after me.'

In the end, the curious locals plied Maloney with sufficient drink to loosen his tongue, enough for him to make a peculiar claim: 'I saw the black elves, over yonder in Bloody Acre, sure as I'm standin' 'ere.'

There was a ripple of hollow forced laughter from a few of those present, but then a cold draught wafted through the pub, across the back of everyone's neck, and silence descended on the assembled company. Maloney was a religious man and always wore his rosary, and he undid the top buttons of his shirt, clutched the rosary beads, and said, 'I swear upon these 'oly beads that I saw black elves ... 'orrible they were!' And there were gasps from some of the drinkers, for they knew now that the Irishman was telling the truth.

Maloney downed a shot of whiskey, then, full of dutch courage, suggested a midnight torch hunt for the elves. Many of the drinkers, also full of ale and spirits, obtained flaming torches, and en masse invaded the cemetery across the road. Staggering and swaying, they walked in a disorderly procession along the low sandstone cemetery wall to see if any of the black elves were knocking about. A fox bolted past the motley file of torch-bearers, and a man fell off the wall in fright, landing amongst a tangle of brambles.

Suddenly, Reverend Warr turned up in his pyjamas, giving them all the fright of their lives. Infuriated by the midnight hunt for elves, of all things, he drove the superstitious locals out of the churchyard, telling them there were no such things as black elves in the acre and to stop being so stupid and gullible.

'Well, I begs to differ there, you see, Father Almighty!' said Maloney, almost setting fire to a friend's clothes with his wavering torch. Reverend Warr accused the Irishman of blasphemy, but Maloney went on unabashed, 'I am prepared to swear on a stack of Bibles ... go and get 'em, Vicar! I, Michael Patrick Maloney, swear by Almighty God that I was chased by elves dressed in black, and armed to the teeth they was, in that field yonder!'

'There's nothing in that field but hares and foxes you stupid drunken Irishman!' said Warr.

Maloney took offence and hopped down from the cemetery wall. 'Oh, I'm not 'avin' that, your holiness. Stupid Irishman, eh? Well, put your money where your mouth is and go across yon acre yerself then! Go on! Prove me a liar!' Maloney said, laying down a challenge, which the vicar had no choice but to accept, because over twenty parishioners were present.

'Very well,' he replied, 'I shall go forth into the acre tomorrow evening, and put an end to all this silliness; now kindly leave this hallowed ground and get to your beds like good Christian men.'

At around 10pm on the following evening, Warr, true to his word, entered the Bloody Acre from the eastern side, via a farmer's field where Hartsbourne Avenue now runs. As a concession, he was allowed to carry a torch which had been dipped in tar. About thirty people watched the vicar squeeze through a gap in the hedge as he entered the mysterious field, which was an overgrown jungle choked with ferns, nettles and weeds. At the other side of the acre, on Score Lane, Maloney waited with a hip flask of whiskey on this cold evening. Dozens of locals waited with him, expecting to see the brave vicar emerge from the field within a few minutes. An enterprising baker sold cakes to the curious mob, and Mrs Rimmer, the landlady of the Childwall Abbey, served alfresco ale to the crowd. It was turning into quite an event and everyone was enjoying the party atmosphere.

Just a few minutes after he had ventured into the acre, the flame of the vicar's torch went out. Half an hour went by, and Reverend George Winter Warr still hadn't shown up. A smug Maloney addressed the crowd. 'Didn't I tell yous there were evil tings afoot in that field? And didn't the Reverend call me a liar? So 'e did.'

A soldier named Talbot, a policeman named Jones, and a butcher named Williams, eventually went into the acre to search for the overdue vicar, but they couldn't find any trace of him. Others joined in the search, but were forced to give up by midnight because of an unseasonal downpour.

That night, the Childwall Abbey pub did a roaring trade, packed with members of the search party, and hordes of curious people who had come to learn more of the vicar's seemingly supernatural disappearance. Michael Maloney didn't have to put his hand in his pocket once that night, because everyone who wanted to hear first hand what he had seen in the acre bought him a drink. Maloney chalked his impression of the black elves on the darts scoreboard, and started to tell ghost stories as the winds of Childwall wailed like a banshee and the rain battered the pub windows.

At nigh on three in the morning, Mrs Rimmer was telling the drinkers they'd have to go home, when there

190

was a loud knocking on the pub door. Everyone went deathly quiet. A tall tailor named Loftus peeped out the window – but could see no one at the door. Yet three more knocks came in quick succession, followed by a groaning voice. The bolt was drawn back by Mrs Rimmer, and everyone backed away from the door.

'Who is it?' Mrs Rimmer called out. There was no answer. She slowly opened the door. Michael Maloney hid behind the bar counter, then peeped over it at the door that was steadily opening. 'They've come for me! Don't let 'em in!' he cried in a slurred voice.

The Reverend Warr lay on the ground outside the pub door in a sorry state. A long tail of his grey hair, which was usually neatly combed over to conceal his extensive baldness, was dangling on one side of his head, and his trousers were missing, as were his shoes and one of his socks. His black clerical jacket was slashed in several places and his white collar was all askew. The crucifix which he always wore round his neck had somehow had its crossbeam broken off and the upright was bent into a horseshoe shape. Warr's eyes were bulging with fear.

Three burly drinkers picked the vicar up off the road and carried him as decorously as they could into the pub, and gently placed him in a padded-leather fireside chair, where, against his will, they administered brandy to him. When he had regained his senses he began to mutter strange things. 'The devils!' he kept repeating over and over. Then, all of a sudden, a hush came over the pub as a rain of taps was heard on the front door. Mr Loftus looked out the window and yelled, 'Gloriana! Look at this!' Everyone rushed to the windows.

In the pale summer predawn light, hundreds of tiny figures, all about three feet in height, were swarming down the cobbled road, some of them carrying spears. They were as black and shiny as a death watch beetle in their strange armour, as they streamed past the pub, headed for the acre, and when they reached that accursed piece of land, they disappeared into it.

From that day until the day he died, in December 1895, aged eighty-one, the vicar refused to tell anyone what had happened to him that evening when he tried to cross the Bloody Acre in Childwall.

Bloody Acre is still uncultivated, and few will venture into it, even today.

~